AQA GCSE

HIGHER PLUS MODULAR

Homework Book

Claire Plass

About this book

This book provides extra exercises for the topics covered in the Higher Plus Student Book. There are four or five exercises for each Student Book chapter. In each, the first exercise (HW1) reviews topics from previous chapters in that Unit; the final exercise reviews the chapter and includes some exam-style questions. The remaining two or three exercises for each chapter give extra practice in the key topics.

Contents

Unit 1

D1	Sampling and averages	1-4
N1	Numbers and arithmetic	5-11
D2	Median and quartiles	12-15
D3	Probability	16-19
N2	Ratio and proportion	20-23
D4	Interpreting frequency graphs	24-28
D5	Independent events	29-32

Unit 2

A1	Expressions	33-37
A2	Sequences and linear graphs	38-42
N3	Written calculations	43-46
A3	Equations and formulae	47-50
N4	Integers and powers	51-55
A4	Quadratic equations and proof	56-59

A5	Inequalities and simultaneous equations	60-63

Unit 3

G1	Circle theorems	64-67
G2	Transformations and congruence	68-72
N5	Proportionality	73-76
G3	Length, area and volume	77-81
G4	Pythagoras and trigonometry	82-86
A6	Further quadratic equations	87-89
G5	Sine and cosine rules	90-94
A7	Sketching graphs	95-98
G6	Vectors	99-102
A8	Transforming graphs	103-106
G7	Trigonometric graphs	107-110

OXFORD
UNIVERSITY PRESS

OXFORD
UNIVERSITY PRESS

Great Clarendon Street, Oxford OX2 6DP

Oxford University Press is a department of the University of Oxford.
It furthers the University's objective of excellence in research, scholarship, and education by
publishing worldwide in

Oxford   New York

Auckland   Cape Town   Dar es Salaam   Hong Kong   Karachi
Kuala Lumpur   Madrid   Melbourne   Mexico City   Nairobi
New Delhi   Shanghai   Taipei   Toronto

With offices in

Argentina   Austria   Brazil   Chile   Czech Republic   France   Greece
Guatemala   Hungary   Italy   Japan   Poland   Portugal   Singapore
South Korea   Switzerland   Thailand   Turkey   Ukraine   Vietnam

© Oxford University Press

The moral rights of the author have been asserted

Database right Oxford University Press (maker)

First published 2011

All rights reserved. No part of this publication may be reproduced,
stored in a retrieval system, or transmitted, in any form or by any means, without the prior
permission in writing of Oxford University Press, or as expressly permitted by law, or under
terms agreed with the appropriate reprographics rights organization. Enquiries concerning
reproduction outside the scope of the above should be sent to the Rights Department, Oxford
University Press, at the address above

You must not circulate this book in any other binding or cover
and you must impose this same condition on any acquirer

British Library Cataloguing in Publication Data

Data available

ISBN 978 0 19912898 3

10 9 8 7 6 5 4 3 2 1

Printed in Great Britain by Bell and Bain Ltd, Glasgow

Cover photo: Karanta/Dreamstime

Mixed Sources
Product group from well-managed
forests and other controlled sources
www.fsc.org   Cert no. TT-COC-002769
© 1996 Forest Stewardship Council

FSC

1 Value Added Tax (VAT) is 17.5%. In some discount stores, prices are given before VAT has been added. To find 17.5% of a number without using a calculator find

- 10% by dividing the number by 10
- 5% by halving the value of 10%
- 2.5% by halving the value of 5%

Then sum together the values.
Work out 17.5% of these prices, rounding to the nearest penny where necessary.

a £120   **b** £80   **c** £36

d £14   **e** £25   **f** £6.50

2 Copy and complete this table.

Fraction	Decimal	Percentage
$\frac{3}{5}$	0.6	60%
$\frac{3}{4}$	0.75	45%
$\frac{11.25}{25}$	0.45	45%
$\frac{3}{10}$	0.$\dot{3}$	30%
$\frac{1}{8}$	0.125	12.5%

3 Here is a set of data on the numbers of cars at a junction in 5 minute periods.

4, 1, 5, 0, 2, 4, 6, 2, 4, 1, 5, 2, 8, 0, 7, 2, 1, 3, 0, 4, 6, 1, 3, 4, 5, 6, 5, 1, 1, 3, 0, 2, 5, 6, 7, 1, 6, 2, 2, 4, 1, 2, 3, 2, 4, 7, 0, 8

Record these data in a frequency table like this.

Number of cars	Tally	Frequency
0		
1		
⋮		
8		
	Total	

1 For each survey, suggest reasons why the chosen sample may be biased.

   a To find out the most popular sport amongst young people by asking teenage boys as they leave a football training academy.

   b To find out the most popular make of car by noting down the cars belonging to people who live on one road in Nottingham.

   c To find out the popularity of school uniforms by telephoning all the households on one page of the telephone directory on a Monday.

   d To find out the preferred choice of music for a school disco by asking the students who leave one of these discos at the end of the night.

2 A machine in a factory produces bottles with screw caps. Every 20th bottle is produced with a cap that does not seal the bottle. A factory worker notices one faulty bottle cap and decides to take a systematic sample of bottles in order to assess the scale of the problem. Explain the effect of sampling

   a every 20th bottle, beginning at bottle number 20

   b every 5th bottle, beginning at bottle number 5

   c every 5th bottle, beginning at bottle number 3.

   Hint: Work out the proportion of faulty bottles in the sample taken and decide on the most likely conclusion of the factory worker.

3 Below is a list of the number of times each of a group of 30 students has visited the school library in the last term.

0	5	8	2	4	4	9	10	0	1
2	9	5	1	6	3	1	1	0	5
12	3	8	1	4	8	2	4	3	2

   Using the random number generator on a calculator, choose a sample of eight of the answers given.

   Hint: Assign a two-digit number to each of the answers above (0 is number 01, 5 is number 02, etc.). Press Ran# on your calculator.

1 Lorna is carrying out a survey in order to establish the popularity of school uniforms at her school. This table shows information about the gender and year group of the students.

	Male	Female
Year 7	100	115
Year 8	108	92
Year 9	88	122
Year 10	83	97
Year 11	124	71

a She decides to choose a stratified sample of 50 students by gender and year group. Work out the numbers of students to be sampled.

b Explain how to choose the male students from year 7.

2 A cattery receives a delivery of 500 pouches of a new brand of cat food: 225 pouches of chicken in jelly, 150 pouches of turkey in gravy and 125 pouches of tuna. Explain how the owners of the cattery could take a stratified sample of 30 pouches in order to test the quality of the cat food.

3 The table below shows the number of letters in the first 50 words of the novel *The Hobbit* by J. R. R. Tolkien.

Word length	1	2	3	4	5	6	7
Frequency	5	11	12	10	7	4	1

a Find the **i** mean **ii** median **iii** mode.
b Calculate the range.

4 Two dice are thrown and the smaller number of the two shown on the dice is subtracted from the larger. The results of 100 throws are shown in the table.

Result	0	1	2	3	4	5
Frequency	18	26	21	14	14	7

a Calculate the median.
b Calculate the interquartile range.

1 Annabel recorded her test results in the back of her exercise book.

Maths	English	Physics	Chemistry	Biology
88%	85%	77%	79%	(blot)

'My mean mark in these five tests was 81%.'
Unfortunately, Annabel noticed that there was an ink blot obscuring her mark in Biology. Can you help her to work out her Biology result?

2 Kath recorded the masses of 50 two-year-olds.

Mass, m (kg)	Frequency	Midpoint	Midpoint × frequency
$10 < m \leqslant 11$	5	10.5	$10.5 \times 5 = 52.5$
$11 < m \leqslant 12$	15	11.5	
$12 < m \leqslant 13$	17		
$13 < m \leqslant 14$	9		
$14 < m \leqslant 15$	4		
Total			

  a Copy and complete the table to find an estimate for the mean.

  b Find

    i the modal class   **ii** the class containing the median.

  c Work out an estimate for the range.

3 The table shows the number of boys and girls in years 12 and 13 of a school.

	Year 12	Year 13
Boys	80	55
Girls	70	75

A teacher wants to find out whether or not to run a ski trip this year and decides to take a stratified sample of 50 pupils. Calculate the numbers of students to be sampled.

1 Simplify these fractions.

a $\frac{25}{100}$ b $\frac{49}{70}$ c $\frac{36}{60}$ d $\frac{18}{90}$

e $\frac{80}{100}$ f $\frac{42}{60}$ g $\frac{24}{66}$ h $\frac{51}{68}$

2 Work out:

a $360 \div 100$ b $496 \div 100$ c 87×100

d 3.2×100 e $275 \div 100$ f $15.2 \div 100$

g $8 \div 100$ h $206 \div 100$ i 37.2×100

3 Michael lists the number of students in each year group at his secondary school.

Year group	7	8	9	10	11
No. of students	240	248	235	252	225

He decides to take a stratified sample of 50 students. How many students from each year group should he choose?

4 A machine producing chocolate cake bars develops a fault. Every 10th cake bar is sub-standard. As a result of a quality control check, a sample of cake bars is taken and none are found to be sub-standard.

Is the sample most likely to have been a random or systematic sample? Explain your answer.

1 Round these numbers to the degree of accuracy given in brackets.

a 1451 (nearest 100)
b 294 (nearest 10)
c 23.56 (nearest whole)
d 34.89 (1 decimal place)
e 2104 (nearest 1000)
f 12.698 (2 decimal places)
g 0.58472 (3 decimal places)
h 1.99 (1 decimal place)

2 Round these numbers to the degree of accuracy given in brackets.

a 1.347 (3 significant figures)
b 12.831 (3 significant figures)
c 0.00453 (2 significant figures)
d 0.3004 (2 significant figures)
e 1239 (2 significant figures)
f 63 920 (1 significant figure)
g 235.95 (4 significant figures)
h 10 957 (3 significant figures)

3 Write the upper and lower bounds for these measurements to the degree of accuracy given.

a 4 m (nearest unit)
b 650 mm (nearest 10)
c 241.3 g (1 decimal place)
d 45 ml (nearest 5 ml)
e 8300 km (2 significant figures)
f 11.53 secs (2 decimal places)

4 Find the upper and lower bounds of these calculations.

a The area of a sheet of paper with length 29.4 cm and width 20.7 cm, measured to the nearest millimetre.
b The speed of a car travelling 164 km, to the nearest kilometre, in 120 minutes, to the nearest minute.

1 These calculations all involve the number 8. State whether the answer to each question will be smaller or larger than 8. You do not have to work out the answers.

  a 8×0.4 **b** 8×1.3 **c** $8 \div 1.5$ **d** $8 \div 0.2$

2 Round each of the values in these calculations to 1 significant figure to produce an estimate. Then match the calculation with its actual answer.

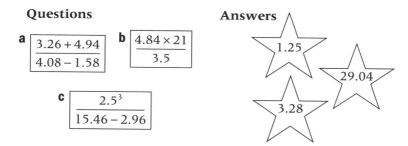

Questions

a $\dfrac{3.26 + 4.94}{4.08 - 1.58}$ **b** $\dfrac{4.84 \times 21}{3.5}$

c $\dfrac{2.5^3}{15.46 - 2.96}$

Answers

1.25

29.04

3.28

3 Two lengths of piping are fastened together.

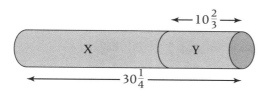

The combined length of the piping is $30\frac{1}{4}$ inches.

The length of piping marked Y is $10\frac{2}{3}$ inches.

Work out the length of the piping marked X.

1 Pair these cards together if they show equivalent decimal numbers and percentages. Which is the odd card out?

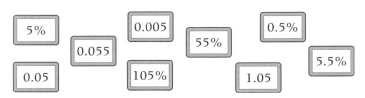

2 True or False?
To work out 109% of a number, multiply by 1.09.
Show your working.

Hint: Use fractions.

3 Arrange these fractions in ascending order.

a $\frac{1}{10}, \frac{2}{5}, \frac{1}{4}, \frac{1}{20}, \frac{3}{4}$

b $\frac{14}{15}, \frac{2}{3}, \frac{2}{5}, \frac{1}{10}, \frac{1}{6}$

c $\frac{5}{12}, \frac{1}{8}, \frac{1}{6}, \frac{2}{3}, \frac{7}{24}$

d $\frac{1}{2}, \frac{2}{5}, \frac{1}{30}, \frac{1}{12}, \frac{7}{15}$

4 Write these fractions, decimals and percentages in descending order.

a 50%, 0.42, 0.07, $\frac{7}{20}$, $\frac{2}{5}$, 12%, 0.9, $\frac{71}{100}$

b 0.7, 28%, 0.09, $\frac{1}{25}$, 37%, 1, 82%, $\frac{11}{20}$

5 Convert $0.\dot{9}$ to a fraction.
What integer is equivalent to this fraction?

1 Write these numbers in standard form.

  a 600   **b** 19 340
  c 2 000 000   **d** 15
  e 17 504   **f** 718 300

2 Write these numbers in standard form.

  a 0.16   **b** 0.00532
  c 0.06001   **d** 0.04
  e 0.0000007 **f** 0.004321

3 Change these numbers in standard form to ordinary numbers.

  a 6.3×10^2 **b** 14.05×10^6
  c 1.934×10^3 **d** 7×10^5
  e 8.3×10^0 **f** 16.4×10^1

4 Change these numbers in standard form to ordinary numbers.

  a 4.8×10^{-2} **b** 6×10^{-5}
  c 2.003×10^{-3} **d** 2.9×10^{-1}
  e 8.999×10^{-8} **f** 1.717×10^{-10}

5 Work these out without using a calculator, giving your answer in standard form.

  a $(8 \times 10^4) \div (4 \times 10^2)$
  b $(9.6 \times 10^{-8}) \div (3 \times 10^{-5})$
  c $(6 \times 10^{-4}) \times (5 \times 10^9)$
  d $(2.4 \times 10^3) \times (5 \times 10^4)$
  e $(3 \times 10^5) \div (6 \times 10^{-2})$

6 In 2004, the Duke of Westborough had an estimated fortune of £2600 million.

  a Express this number in standard form.
  b If the Duke decides to share his fortune equally amongst the 6×10^7 people in the United Kingdom work out how much each person receives, to the nearest penny.

1 Jonathan took measurements around his school.
Are these values sensible?

   a The height of the cherry tree outside the maths
building = 4.5 m.

   b The weight of an apple from the school canteen = 1.6 kg.

   c The height of the door into the French room = 215 cm.

   d The capacity of the sink in the wash room = 2.3 litres.

2 Write the upper and lower bounds of these calculations.

   a The radius of a circle measured as 4.5 cm to 1 decimal
place.

   b The area of a rectangle with dimensions 12 cm and 6.8 cm
taken to 2 significant figures.

   c The width of a parallelogram which has an area of 20 cm^2
(to the nearest square centimetre) and a length of 8.45 cm
(to 2 decimal places).

   d The speed, in km/h, of a car which travels 35 km (to the
nearest kilometre) in 30 minutes (to the nearest minute).

3 Use a calculator to evaluate these. Give each answer to an
appropriate degree of accuracy by considering the degree of
accuracy in the question.

   a $(5.2 \times 10^6) \times (8.2 \times 10^3)$ b $(3.45 \times 10^4) \div (1.52 \times 10^{-2})$

   c $(8.35 \times 10^8) \times (6.12 \times 10^{-5})$ d $(7.1 \times 10^3) \div (8.7 \times 10^5)$

4 Find the value of these using a calculator. Give each answer
to an appropriate degree of accuracy by considering the
degree of accuracy in the question.

   a $\sqrt{41.2^2 + 7.62^2}$ b $\sqrt{1.3^2 + 2.7^2 - 2 \times 1.3 \times 2.7}$

   c $4\frac{1}{3} \div 1\frac{3}{7}$ d $\dfrac{-7 + \sqrt{7^2 - (4 \times 3 \times -6)}}{2 \times 3}$

1 Work these out using pencil and paper methods.

a $\frac{1}{2} + \frac{3}{4}$ **b** $1\frac{1}{3} - \frac{2}{7}$

c $4 \times \frac{3}{5}$ **d** $2\frac{3}{4} \div 2\frac{1}{4}$

e 4.52×7.9 **f** $13.5 \div 0.75$

g $436.8 + 19.56$ **h** 32.5% of 140

i 28% of 225   **j** 129 as a percentage of 64

2 a Use approximations to estimate the value of

$$\frac{458 \times 0.036}{1.69}$$

Show all of your working.

b Use your calculator to find the exact answer.

c Calculate the percentage error for the approximation.

Hint: Round each number to 1 significant figure.

3 Rupert decides to send a red rose to his girlfriend. The rose measures 30 cm, to the nearest centimetre. Rupert buys a presentation box of length 30.1 cm, measured to the nearest millimetre.

a Explain why the rose may not fit inside the box.

b What is the maximum length that Rupert may have to cut from the stem of the rose in order to make it fit in the box?

4 Using the fact that

$$56 \times 421 = 23\,576$$

write the answer to these calculations.

a 5.6×42.1

b $0.56 \times 421\,000$

c $23.576 \div 5.6$

5 Change these numbers in standard form to ordinary numbers.

a 3.6×10^3 **b** 5.91×10^{-5}

c 2.15×10^{-1} **d** 9.009×10^2

1 Work out

   a $1\frac{1}{4} \times 2\frac{2}{3}$ b $2\frac{1}{2} \div 1\frac{1}{3}$ c $5\frac{3}{7} \times 3\frac{1}{2}$ d $2\frac{5}{8} \div 1\frac{3}{4}$

2 Round these numbers to the degree of accuracy given in brackets.

   a 4.329 (2 decimal places)
   b 3.825 (2 significant figures)
   c 0.21563 (3 decimal places)
   d 0.00185 (1 significant figure)
   e 10 214 (3 significant figures)
   f 1.20045 (4 significant figures)
   g 1.995 (2 decimal places)
   h 45 126 (2 significant figures)

3 Use standard form approximations to find an estimate for these calculations.

   a $(81\ 500 \div 194)^3$ b $\dfrac{4420 \times 0.8}{0.52 \times 0.043}$

   c Use your calculator to find the exact answers to parts a and b.

4 Charlotte carries out a survey to find out whether or not people belong to a gym. She asks all the people at her hockey club.

   a Write down two reasons as to why this is not a good way to find out whether or not people belong to a gym.

   b Devise a question that Charlotte could ask in order to find out how often people use a gym.

1 Elsie recorded the height, in centimetres, of each of the eleven sunflowers in her garden. She put the heights in order.

130 132 134 138 140 140 142 146 148 150 152

 a Find
  i the lower quartile
  ii the upper quartile.
 b Draw a box plot for these data.

2 Harry summarised the heights of the large number of 'Queen Elizabeth' rose bushes planted in his garden.

Smallest: 94 cm	Lower Quartile: 106 cm	Median: 118 cm
Tallest: 135 cm	Upper Quartile: 124 cm	

Draw a box plot for the data.

3 The heights, h, in centimetres, of 120 'Peace' rose bushes are given in the table.

Height, h cm	Frequency
$110 < h \leqslant 115$	32
$115 < h \leqslant 120$	44
$120 < h \leqslant 125$	22
$125 < h \leqslant 130$	13
$130 < h \leqslant 135$	8
$135 < h \leqslant 140$	1

 a Draw a cumulative frequency table for the data.
 b Draw a cumulative frequency diagram for the data.

1 The table gives information concerning the examination results of a group of 100 students.

a Draw a cumulative frequency table and diagram for these data.
b Estimate
  i the median
  ii the interquartile range from the graph.
c Estimate the number of students that passed the examination if the pass mark was 55%.

Test result, $t\%$	Frequency
$40 < t \leqslant 50$	5
$50 < t \leqslant 60$	20
$60 < t \leqslant 70$	34
$70 < t \leqslant 80$	27
$80 < t \leqslant 90$	12
$90 < t \leqslant 100$	2

2 The table gives information concerning the lifetime in hours, h, of 120 light bulbs.

a Draw a cumulative frequency table and diagram for these data.
b Use the graph to estimate
  i the number of light bulbs with a lifetime of 975 hours or less
  ii the number of light bulbs with a lifetime of more than 1075 hours.
c Find
  i the median
  ii the lower and upper quartiles.
d Use your results to draw a box plot.

Hours, h	Frequency
$900 < h \leqslant 950$	6
$950 < h \leqslant 1000$	18
$1000 < h \leqslant 1050$	40
$1050 < h \leqslant 1100$	28
$1100 < h \leqslant 1150$	16
$1150 < h \leqslant 1200$	12

Hint: Use lower bound of first class and upper bound of last class to estimate the minimum and maximum as they are not given.

1 The graph shows the waiting times for two MOT 'sit and wait' test centres.

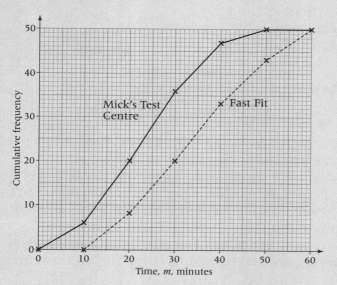

a Write down three comparisons concerning the waiting times at 'Mick's Test Centre' and 'Fast Fit'.

b Use the graphs above to find
  i the median for each of the two test centres.
  ii the lower and upper quartiles for each of the two test centres.

c Use your results to draw two box plots.

2 These are the warmest January temperatures for the decade 1920-29 as measured in Wick and Southampton.

Wick: 5.8   7.2 4.9 7.1 6.1 6.6 6.3 6.2 5.7 4.8
S'ton: 8.6 10.2 8.0 8.9 8.4 9.1 8.1 8.2 9.3 4.4

a Show the data on a back-to-back stem-and leaf diagram.

b Write two comparisons between the data sets.

D3 HW1 Check-in review

1 Ashim draws this picture on a piece of paper measuring 12 cm by 8 cm. He colours the six circles red and the rest of the paper blue. Calculate the area of the paper that is blue.

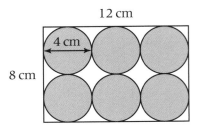

Hint: The area A of a circle of radius r is given by $A = \pi r^2$.

2 Find the upper and lower bounds of these calculations.

a The area of a rectangular pond with length 4 m and width 3 m, measured to the nearest centimetre.

b The range of temperature during one day in Derby if the maximum recorded temperature was 28 °C and the minimum recorded temperature was 18 °C, to the nearest degree Celsius.

c The density of a piece of metal if its mass is 1125 g, to the nearest gram and its volume is 150 cm³, to the nearest cubic centimetre.

3 This table shows the time taken in minutes by a group of 40 Mathematics teachers to solve a Sudoku puzzle.

Time, t	$0 \leqslant t < 5$	$5 \leqslant t < 10$	$10 \leqslant t < 15$	$15 \leqslant t < 20$	$20 \leqslant t < 25$
Frequency	2	6	12	7	3

Use this information to find
a the modal class
b the class containing the median time
c an estimate of the mean time.

1 A child's push chair is available in five different fabrics. These fabrics and the probability with which they are selected by a consumer are shown in the table.

Neutrals	Checks	City Chic	Vibrant	Pure
0.42	0.11	x	$2x$	0.05

Find the missing value x and hence the missing probabilities.

2 A child has a set of building blocks, numbered 1 to 20, in a trolley. The child selects one block at random.

a Find the probability that the number on the chosen block is
   i an 8   **ii** a multiple of 4   **iii** a factor of 6
   iv a prime number   **v** the number 3 or greater than 15.

b What can you say about the pair of events in part **v**?

3 A biased dice is in the shape of a tetrahedron. The dice is rolled 100 times. The table shows the outcomes of this experiment.

Score	1	2	3	4
Frequency	48	19	16	17

a If the dice is rolled once more, find the probability that it will land on a   **i** 1   **ii** 3 or 4   **iii** not 2.

b The dice is to be rolled 300 times. How many times would you expect the dice to land on a   **i** 2   **ii** 1 or 4?

4 80 students are asked to choose their favourite season.

	Spring	Summer	Autumn	Winter	Total
Skiers	8			12	
Non-skiers		18	7	8	
Total	20		16		80

a Copy and complete the table.

b A student is chosen at random. Find the probability the student
   i prefers summer   **ii** is a skier who prefers winter.

1 Joan carries out a statistical experiment.
She throws a dice 100 times. She scores a five 30 times.
Is the dice fair? Explain your answer.

2 A dice is rolled 30 times in order to test its fairness.
The results of this experiment are shown below.

1	3	3	5	6	2	4	4	5	2
4	2	1	4	5	1	6	4	4	4
2	3	5	4	6	4	1	5	6	4

  a Work out the relative frequency of rolling each number.
  b Is the dice biased? Explain your answer.
  c What could you do to improve the experiment?

3 A spinner has equally sized sections numbered 1 to 8.
The spinner is spun and a fair coin is thrown.

  a Draw a table to show all possible outcomes.
  b Find the probability of obtaining
    i the number 2 and a head
    ii a number greater than 5 and a tail
    iii an even number and a tail
    iv a prime number and a head.

4 A bag contains 4 red counters and 6 black counters.
A counter is drawn at random, its colour noted and then
replaced in the bag. A second counter is then drawn.

  a Find the probability of obtaining
    i a red counter on the first draw followed by a black
      counter on the second
    ii two red counters.
  b What can you say about the events 'a red counter on the
    first draw' and 'a black counter on the second'?
  c If the first counter is not replaced before the second
    counter is drawn, what can you now say about the events
    'a red counter on the first draw' and 'a black counter on
    the second'? Explain your answer.

1 Jason and Clare play two games of Scrabble.
The probability that Jason will win any game against
Clare is 0.55. Work out the probability that Jason wins at
least one game.

2 Lorna has two tins of pencils.
Tin A contains 5 red, 6 blue and 4 yellow pencils.
Tin B contains 3 red, 4 blue and 5 yellow pencils.
Lorna chooses one pencil at random from each tin.
Calculate the probability that the chosen pencils are
different colours.

3 Cameron carries out a survey about the words in a book.
He chooses a page at random and counts the letters in
the first 150 words on that page. The table shows the
outcomes of his experiment.

Number of letters	1	2	3	4	5	6	7	8
Frequency	8	14	35	45	30	10	5	3

The book has 30 000 words.
Estimate the number of 3-letter words in the book.

4 The table shows information about the teachers in a
school.

	≤5 years at school	>5 years at school
Male	20	30
Female	15	10

    a Two teachers are to be chosen at random to accept
    an award for their school. One male and one female
    teacher are to be chosen. Calculate the probability that
    they will both have worked at the school for ≤5 years.
    b It is later decided to choose one teacher with ≤5 years
    service and one with >5 years service to the school.
    Calculate the probability that both teachers are male.

1 The table shows the number of tea bags in 100 boxes marked 'average contents 80 tea bags'. Does the claim appear to be correct if the mean average is considered?

No. of bags	77	78	79	80	81	82	83
Frequency	5	12	23	32	18	9	1

2 By rounding each of the values in these calculations to 1 significant figure, find an approximate answer.

a $\dfrac{86.7 - 21.4}{5.95 + 4.18}$ **b** $\dfrac{42.71 \times 0.099}{2.03^3}$

c $\sqrt{\dfrac{18.2^2}{0.82 \times 4.56}}$ **d** $\dfrac{3.1^4}{0.088 - 0.008\,76}$

3 Isla and William are playing a computer game. They record the time (in seconds) that it takes to complete each round and compile the information shown in the table.

	Isla	Wiliam
Median	64	59
Lower quartile	50	44
Upper quartile	71	73
Minimum	45	40
Maximum	75	82

  a Draw box plots for each set of information on the same axes.

  b Comment on and compare the performances of Isla and William.

4 Write 0.36 as a fraction.

1 In a primary school class, $\frac{1}{5}$ of the students have black hair, $\frac{3}{10}$ of the students have blonde hair and $\frac{7}{15}$ of the students have brown hair. The rest have red hair.

  a What proportion of the class have red hair?
  b If there are 30 students in the class, how many have
    i black hair   **ii** brown hair?

2 Calculate:

  a 10% of 90 km
  b 28% of 170 litres
  c 15% of 70 cm
  d 7% of 42 kg
  e 8% of 60 kg
  f 34% of 60 litres

3 In a sale, a handbag costing £40 is reduced by 20%. What is the sale price?

4 The gym membership fee increases by 12%. What is the new fee for:

  a standard membership, previously £20 per month
  b gold membership, previously £32 per month
  c platinum membership, previously £37.50 per month.

5 Zac bought a van for £15 000. Each year the van depreciated by 5%. Work out the value of Zac's van 2 years after he purchased it.

1 Philip's van depreciates in value by 8% each year. After four years the van is worth £9170.

   a What was the original cost of the van?

   b What was the overall percentage depreciation of the van after 4 years?

   c If the van continues to depreciate at the same rate, after how many years will the van be worth less than £5000?

2 A jacket cost £350.
In the sale it cost £325.
What was the percentage reduction?

3 In a sale, all prices are reduced by 15%.
A TV in the sale costs £679.15 what was the original price of the TV?

4 Mike wants to invest £200 for five years. His bank offers him two options:

Option 1 is simple interest of 5.25% per annum.
Option 2 is compound interest of 5% per annum.

Which option should Mike choose in order to achieve the most interest on his investment? Show all your working.

5 Sam buys a new jacket from his favourite shop.
The shop offers Sam a 20% discount as a loyalty reward.
Sam accepts the discount and pays £64 for the jacket.
What was the price of the jacket *before* the discount was applied?

1 **a** Divide £350 in the ratio 3 : 4.
   b Divide £950 in the ratio 8 : 11.

2 In the UK in 2001 there were 95 males for every
   100 females in the population.

   a Write this as a ratio of males to females.
      Give your answer in its simplest terms.
   b What proportion of the population was female?
      Give your answer as a fraction in its simplest form.
   c If there were 58.8 million people in the UK in 2001,
      how many males were there? Give your answer to
      3 significant figures.

3 In a class, the ratio of girls to boys is 5 : 4. There are
   15 girls in this class. Work out the number of boys.

4 Two work colleagues, Bill and Ben, share a bonus of
   £5000 in the ratio 3 : 2. Ben decides to share his portion
   of the money between himself and the two members of
   his support team in the ratio 5 : 2 : 1.
   How much does Ben take home?

5 In 2001, Britain had a population of 58.8 million. If the
   population of Britain is increasing at, on average, an
   annual rate of 0.4%, calculate an estimate for the
   population of Britain in 2005. Give your answer to
   3 significant figures.

1 Five coins are tossed and the number of heads is recorded each time. The results of 200 tosses are shown in the table below.

Number of heads	0	1	2	3	4	5
Frequency	8	30	58	62	34	8

   a Calculate the median.
   b Calculate the interquartile range.

2 Explain why rounding each of the values in these calculations to 1 significant figure would *not* be an appropriate method for estimating the answer.

   a $\dfrac{21.4 \times 5.15}{0.84 - 0.75}$ b $(4.56 - 4.32)^2$

3 Angela, Rajat and Ayesha have savings in the ratio 5 : 4 : 1. If Rajat has £2400, calculate the amount of money that Angela and Ayesha have in savings.

4 Lynda is looking for her reading glasses. The probability that they are in her handbag is $\frac{3}{5}$. The probability that they are by her bed is $\frac{2}{9}$. Find the probability that Lynda's reading glasses are

   a either in her handbag or by her bed
   b lost! That is, in neither of these places.

   What assumption have you made throughout this question?

1 A class of 30 students is challenged to time one minute. The students are asked to stand and then sit down after they believe one minute has passed. These are the actual times, in seconds, at which they sat down.

75 53 72 77 59 42 65 52 70 58 70 45 63 41 49
58 62 43 48 57 61 55 62 59 68 73 63 61 67 71

  a Construct a frequency table for the data.
  b Construct a frequency polygon for the data.

2 The table gives information about the time spent eating breakfast by a group of 100 people aged 20–34.

Time, t, min	Frequency	Class width	Frequency density
$0 < t \leqslant 5$	20	5	$20 \div 5 = 4$
$5 < t \leqslant 10$	38		
$10 < t \leqslant 30$	24		
$30 < t \leqslant 40$	10		
$40 < t \leqslant 60$	8		

  a Copy and complete the table.
  b Draw a histogram for the data.

3 The frequency table shows the time spent completing homework by a sample of students one Monday evening.

Time, t, hours	$0 < t \leqslant 0.5$	$0.5 < t \leqslant 1$	$1 < t \leqslant 2$	$2 < t \leqslant 2.5$	$2.5 < t \leqslant 3$
Frequency	56	32	32	10	6

  a Complete a histogram for the data.
  b How many students spent half an hour or less on their homework?
  c How many students were in the sample?

1 This incomplete table and histogram give information about the length of 100 babies at birth.

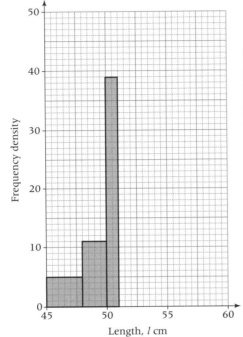

Length, l, cm	Frequency
$45 < l \leq 48$	
$48 < l \leq 50$	
$50 < l \leq 51$	
$51 < l \leq 54$	18
$54 < l \leq 56$	6

a Use the histogram to complete the table.
b Copy and complete the histogram.

2 Work out the height of the second bar in each of these histograms in terms of f.

a

Length, l, cm	Frequency	Bar height
$0 < l \leq 20$	16	4 cm
$20 < l \leq 60$	f	

b

Time, t, min	Frequency	Bar height
$0 < t \leq 15$	10	3 cm
$15 < t \leq 60$	f	

1 In 1929 Edwin Hubble published a study of the relationship between how far away a galaxy is, measured in Megaparsecs (Mpc), and how fast it appears to be moving away from us, measured in km/s. Here is some of his data

Speed	0.03	0.28	0.62	0.68	0.91	1.05	1.4	1.63	2
Distance	50	−115	375	200	525	740	750	710	900

a i Plot the data on a scatter graph.
  ii Describe any correlation you see.
b i Draw a line of best fit.
  ii The Southern pinwheel galaxy was measured to be 0.9 Mpc away, predict its speed away from us.
  iii The galaxy Messier 106 was measured to be moving away from us at 500 km/s, predict its distance.
c The quasar 3C 273 has been measured to be moving away from us at 47 000 km/s, can you predict its distance? Explain your answer.

2 The following data show the brightness of the star delta Cephei measured over a number of days.

Time (hours)	0	16	48	64	92	100	112
Brightness	4.32	4.19	3.95	3.85	3.61	3.65	3.85
Time (hours)	120	130	160	200	215	245	260
Brightness	4.10	4.30	4.05	3.75	3.60	3.98	4.29

a Plot this data on a graph.
b Comment on any patterns in the data.

1 Hermione recorded the lengths, in minutes, of all the children's television programmes shown on terrestrial television during one weekday and displayed them in a histogram.

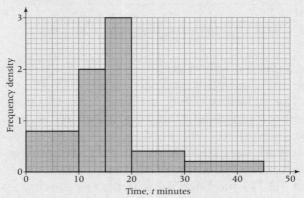

Ten children's programmes lasted more than 10 minutes but less than or equal to 15 minutes.

a Use the information in the histogram to copy and complete the table.

Time, t, min	$0 < t \leqslant 10$	$10 < t \leqslant 15$	$15 < t \leqslant 20$	$20 < t \leqslant 30$	$30 < t \leqslant 45$
Frequency		10			

Hermione repeated her task the next day and produced this table.

Time, t, min	Frequency	Height of bar
$0 < t \leqslant 20$	30	6 cm
$20 < t \leqslant 45$	f	

b Find the height of the second bar in this histogram in terms of f.

1 In the summer sale, all clothes have a 20% discount.

   a What is the sale price of a pair of trousers that cost £85 before the sale?

In the last week of the sale, these sale prices are reduced by a further 20%.

   b What is the price of the trousers now?

   c What is the overall percentage reduction of the pair of trousers after both discounts have been applied?

2 Write these fractions, decimals and percentages in ascending order.

   a $\frac{4}{7}$, 0.23, 16%, 11%, 0.05, $\frac{11}{16}$, 25%, $\frac{2}{9}$

   b 0.75, $\frac{1}{13}$, 18%, $\frac{4}{5}$, 28%, 0.03, $\frac{4}{15}$, 0.4

3 Grace has a toothbrush holder that is 20.2 cm long, to the nearest millimetre. She buys a new toothbrush that measures 20 cm to the nearest centimetre. Explain why Grace's new toothbrush may not fit into her toothbrush holder.

4 Lucy is offered a biscuit from each of two tins.
The first tin contains 6 chocolate and 4 plain biscuits.
The second tin contains 5 chocolate and 10 plain biscuits.
Lucy chooses one biscuit at random from each tin. Calculate the probability that the chosen biscuits are different types.

5 Bob has two boxes of whiteboard pens.

Box number 1 contains 6 pens: 3 red, 2 blue and 1 black.
Box number 2 contains 12 pens: 5 red, 4 blue and 3 black.

Bob chooses one pen at random from each box. Calculate the probability that the chosen pens are different colours.

1　An artist has a box of watercolour paints containing 4 pans of cadmium red colour and 6 pans of cobalt blue colour. In order to paint an abstract picture, the artist chooses a pan of colour at random from the box. He paints with this colour and then chooses a second pan of colour at random.

   a Copy and complete the tree diagram to show all possible outcomes.

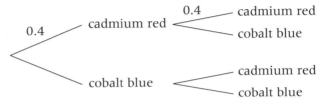

   b Find the probability that the artist chooses cobalt blue both times.

2　A tin contains 12 coloured pencils: 8 yellow and 4 green. A pencil is chosen at random from the tin, used to create a drawing and then replaced. A second pencil is then drawn from the tin at random.

   a Draw a tree diagram to show all possible outcomes.
   b Find the probability that the two pencils chosen are
     i both yellow   **ii** one of each colour.
   c Find the probability that at least one of the pencils chosen is green.

3　Bag A contains 7 white marbles and 3 black marbles. Bag B contains 2 white marbles and 4 red marbles. A marble is chosen at random from each bag.

   a Draw a tree diagram to show all possible outcomes.
   b Find the probability that the two marbles chosen are different colours.
   c Find the probability that at least one of the marbles chosen is red.

1 A box contains 10 chocolate biscuits and 5 plain biscuits. Iona chooses a biscuit at random and eats it. She then chooses a second biscuit at random and eats it.

  a Copy and complete the tree diagram to show all possible outcomes.

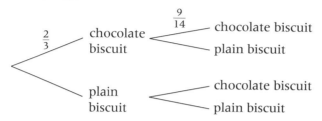

  b Find the probability that Iona chooses to eat
     i two plain biscuits   **ii** one of each type of biscuit.
  c Find the probability that at least one of the biscuits chosen is chocolate.

2 A teacher requires two classroom monitors to be in charge of the register. Two students are to be chosen at random from a class of 25 students: 15 boys and 10 girls.

  a Draw a tree diagram to show all possible outcomes.
  b Find the probability that the two students chosen are
     i both girls   **ii** a boy or a girl, in any order.
  c Find the probability that at least one of the students chosen is a boy.

3 The probability that Ava eats breakfast is 0.4. If Ava eats breakfast, the probability that she is late for school is 0.3 If Ava does not eat breakfast, the probability that she is late for school is 0.1

  a Draw a tree diagram to show all possible outcomes.
  b Work out the probability that on any one day, Ava will *not* be late for school.

1 Wedding guests are given a choice of either 'Aberdeen Angus Fillet Steak with a whisky and cream sauce' or 'Roast Pave of Scottish Salmon with a mushroom sauce'. The table shows the choices of 100 guests.

	Steak	Salmon	Total
Male	42	18	60
Female	16	24	40
Total	58	42	100

  a One wedding guest is to be chosen at random. What is the probability that this guest is female?

  b One of the male guests is chosen at random. What is the probability that he chooses the Steak?

  c One of the guests who chose the Salmon is to be picked at random. What is the probability that they are female?

2 To start a game, a double-six must be obtained on the throw of two fair dice.

  a When any one fair dice is thrown, what is the probability of *not* obtaining a six?

  b Draw a tree diagram to show the two events 'six' and 'not six' for each of the two fair dice.

  c Calculate the probability of obtaining at least one six.

  d Calculate the probability of obtaining a double-six.

3 Isobel sits a multiple choice test with three questions. Each question has five possible answers. Isobel chooses the answer to each question at random. In order to pass the test, Isobel must correctly answer at least two of the three questions.

  a What is the probability that Isobel will correctly answer a question?

  b Draw a tree diagram to show all possible outcomes.

  c Find the probability that Isobel passes the test.

1 Alice surveys her primary school class and finds that 21 out of the 30 children have at least one sibling and 12 of the children do not have a pet. Give your answers as fractions in their lowest terms.

    a What proportion of the children have at least one sibling?
    b What proportion of the children have a pet?
    c What is the ratio of children with siblings to children without siblings? Give this ratio in its simplest form.

2 The table shows the number of words in each of the first 50 sentences of the novel *Pride and Prejudice* by Jane Austen.

    a Calculate an estimate for the mean number of words per sentence.
    b Is the mean a good representation of the average number of words per sentence? Explain your answer.

No. of words per sentence	Frequency
1–10	24
11–20	15
21–30	7
31–40	1
41–50	2
51–60	0
61–70	0
71–80	1

3 Evaluate these expressions when $a = 2$, $b = -3$ and $c = 0.5$

    a $2ab$ **b** $3bc$ **c** $\frac{b + a}{c}$

    d $\frac{4ac}{b^2}$ **e** $5b(c + a)$ **f** $\frac{6c - 2a}{5 - b}$

4 Arrange these fractions, decimals and percentages in ascending order.

    a $\frac{3}{5}$, $\frac{1}{4}$, 32%, 0.57, 0.2

    b 15%, $\frac{1}{5}$, 0.152, $\frac{2}{9}$, $\frac{4}{11}$

1 Simplify these expressions.

a $x^2 \times x^5$ b $y^{-3} \div y^4$

c $\dfrac{t^2}{t^3}$ d $\dfrac{a^3 \times a^5}{a}$

e $(b^{-2})^4$ f $\dfrac{2x^3 \times 3x^6}{x^4}$

g $5p^3 \times 2p^2q$ h $(4m^{-2})^3$

2 If $a = 3^2$ and $b = 3^5$ work these out, leaving your answer as an index number.

a ab b $\dfrac{a}{b}$ c a^2 d ab^2 e $(3b)^2$

3 Expand and simplify these expressions.

a $4(3x + 7)$ b $2y(4x - 1)$

c $6(2p + 1) - 4(p + 9)$ d $x^2(2 + x^3)$

e $(x + 3)(x + 9)$ f $(3x + 4)(x - 5)$

g $(2t - 9)^2$ h $(3 - m)(m + 4) + (2m - 1)^2$

4 Given that two consecutive numbers can be written as $2n$ and $2n + 1$, prove that the sum of the squares of any two consecutive numbers is an odd number.

1 Factorise these by removing common factors.

  a $6p + 3$ **b** $12x - 15$

  c $3xy + 2x$ **d** $4y^2 + 12y^3 + xy$

  e $2pq^2 + 5p^2q$ **f** $6a^3b - 3a^2 + 12$

  g $2(x + y) - (x + y)^2$ **h** $wx + wy - 3x - 3y$

2 Factorise each of these fully.

  a $x^2 + 6x + 5$ **b** $x^2 + 7x - 18$

  c $x^2 - 3x - 18$ **d** $x^2 - 15x - 100$

  e $x^2 - 21x + 110$ **f** $x^2 - 16x + 64$

  g $3x^2 + 21x + 30$ **h** $x^3 - 6x^2 - 40x$

  Hint: You may have to use double brackets and common factors.

3 Factorise each of these using double brackets.

  a $2x^2 + 11x + 5$ **b** $3x^2 + 11x + 6$

  c $5x^2 + 6x - 8$ **d** $6x^2 + 11x + 3$

  e $12x^2 - 23x + 5$ **f** $15x^2 + 34x + 15$

4 Copy and complete each of these.

  a $\Box - 7x - x^2 = (2 \Box x)(x + 9)$

  b $15 + \Box - 2x^2 = (\Box - x)(2x + 5)$

  c $19x - 10 - \Box = (5 - 2x)(3x - \Box)$

1 Simplify these fractions fully and find the odd one out.

$$\frac{18x}{6}$$ $$\frac{15x^2}{5x}$$ $$\frac{6abx}{2ab}$$ $$\frac{4x - 12x^2}{4x}$$ $$\frac{6x^2 + 3x}{2x + 1}$$

2 Simplify these fractions fully.

a $\dfrac{x + 1}{x^2 + 3x + 2}$ **b** $\dfrac{x^2 + 4x - 21}{x - 3}$ **c** $\dfrac{x - 2}{x^2 - 4}$

d $\dfrac{x^2 - 3x - 18}{x^2 - 10x + 24}$ **e** $\dfrac{x^2 - 8x}{x^2 - 3x - 40}$

3 Simplify these fractional multiplications and divisions.

a $\dfrac{2x}{3} \times \dfrac{3}{4}$ **b** $\dfrac{8xy}{9} \times \dfrac{3}{y}$ **c** $\dfrac{x}{5} \div \dfrac{x}{3}$

d $\dfrac{x + 1}{4} \times \dfrac{3}{x^2 + 6x + 5}$ **e** $\dfrac{x^2 - 9}{12} \div \dfrac{x^2 + x - 12}{6}$

4 Simplify each of these.

a $\dfrac{2a}{5} + \dfrac{a}{5}$ **b** $\dfrac{2x}{3} + \dfrac{x}{6}$ **c** $\dfrac{3}{p} - \dfrac{4}{q}$

d $\dfrac{x + 3}{4} + \dfrac{x + 7}{4}$ **e** $\dfrac{2x + 1}{5} - \dfrac{3x + 2}{3}$ **f** $\dfrac{4}{a + 2} - \dfrac{3}{a - 3}$

5 A rectangle has length $= \dfrac{3a^2 - 5a - 2}{12}$ and width $= \dfrac{4}{3a + 1}$.
Its area is 1 cm². Find the dimensions of the rectangle.

1 Factorise

   a $x^2 - 64$ **b** $m^2 - 25$ **c** $49 - t^2$

   d $a^2 - b^2$ **e** $9y^2 - 100$ **f** $x^2 - \dfrac{1}{9}$

   g $25a^2 - \dfrac{4}{9}$ **h** $2a^3 - 32a$

2 **a** Simplify

    i $\dfrac{p^3}{p^4}$ **ii** $\dfrac{2q^2 \times 5q^5}{q^4}$

   b Expand and simplify

    i $(3x + 4)(x - 5)$ **ii** $(3x - y)^2$

3 The area of this trapezium is 525 m².

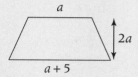

   a Show that $2a^2 + 5a - 525 = 0$.
   b Factorise the left hand side of $2a^2 + 5a - 525 = 0$.

4 $a = 3^x$ and $b = 3^y$.
   Express in terms of a and/or b

   a 3^{x+y} **b** 3^{2x} **c** 3^{y-1}

5 Use the formula average speed = $\dfrac{\text{distance}}{\text{time}}$ to find the speed in km per hour of a car that travelled 25 km in 20 minutes.

6 Writ each expression as a single fraction

   a $\dfrac{6}{x + 2} + \dfrac{5}{x - 3}$ **b** $\dfrac{4}{7x} + \dfrac{3}{7x^2}$

1 Factorise these expressions.

   a $x^2 - 9$ **b** $p^2 - 49$ **c** $4n^2 - 81$

   d $x^2 - \frac{4}{25}$ **e** $3a^3 - 12a$

2 Increase 432 m by 12%.

3 Samantha spends $\frac{3}{5}$ of her monthly salary on tax, her mortgage and her regular bills. She spends $\frac{1}{6}$ of her monthly salary on food bills and $\frac{1}{12}$ on her car payments. The rest she spends on shoes.

   a What proportion of her monthly salary does Samantha spend on shoes?

   b If Samantha earns £2400 a month, write down the amounts that she pays for

      i tax, mortgage and bills   **ii** shoes.

4 The population of the Netherlands is approximately 16.4×10^6 people.

   a Write this number given in standard form as an ordinary number.

   The Netherlands has an area of approximately 41 000 km².

   b Write this number in standard form.

   c Work out the population density **without** using a calculator, giving your answer in standard form.

A2 HW2   Generating sequences and the *n*th term

1 Generate the first five terms of each of these sequences and comment on the behaviour of each.

  a $T_n = 5n - 3$ **b** $T_n = n(n + 1)$ **c** $T_n = 1 + \frac{1}{n}$

  d $T_n = n^2 + 5n + 4$ **e** $T_n = (-2)^{n-1}$

Hint: Use the words diverge, converge, limit and oscillate.

2 Find the value of n that generates the term given from each of these sequences.

  a $T_n = 6n - 1$; $T_n = 59$ **b** $T_n = (n - 1)^2$; $T_n = 49$
  c $T_n = 5(n + 1)$; $T_n = 75$ **d** $T_n = n^3 + 4$; $T_n = 68$

Hint: Form an equation by letting the *n*th term and the term itself equal one another.

3 Match each *n*th term formula with a pictorial sequence.

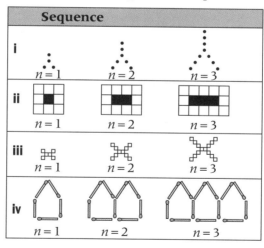

*n*th term	
a	$T = 4n + 1$
b	$T = 3n + 1$
c	$T = 4n + 2$
d	$T = 2(n + 3)$

4 Find the *n*th term of these sequences.

  a 6, 11, 16, 21, 26, ...   **b** 20, 17, 14, 11, 8, ...
  c $\frac{1}{7}, \frac{2}{11}, \frac{3}{15}, \frac{4}{19}, \frac{5}{23}, \ldots$ **d** 5, −1, −7, −13, −19 ...

1 Which of these lines passes through the point (2, 3)?

Line	✓ or ✗
$y = x + 1$	
$3y = 2x + 1$	
$2y = x + 4$	
$y = 4x - 5$	
$y = 5 - 2x$	

2 Which of these lines is parallel to the line $y = 2x + 3$?

Line	✓ or ✗
$y = 3x + 2$	
$y = 2x - 1$	
$2y = x - 3$	
$2y = 4x + 3$	
$3y - 2 = 6x$	

3 Find the gradient of
   a AB
   b BC
   c DC
   d AD.

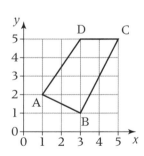

4 Sketch each of these line graphs on a separate set of axes.

   a $y = 3x + 2$ **b** $2y = x + 4$ **c** $y = 5 - x$

5 Find the equation of a line which is parallel to $y = 3x + 6$ and passes through

   a (0, −2)   **b** (2, 5)   **c** (4, 1)

1 Find the equation of a line that is parallel to the line

   a $y = 4 - 2x$ **b** $2y = x + 6$ **c** $y = \frac{1}{3}x + 4$

2 **a** Sketch the line graph $2y = x - 6$.
   b Find the equation of a line which is parallel to $2y = x - 6$
      and passes through (4, 4). Sketch this new line on the
      same set of axes.

3 **a** Without drawing the graphs, write where these pairs of
      lines intersect.
     i $x = 1$ and $y = 7$
     ii $y = -2$ and $x = 5$
     iii $x = \frac{3}{8}$ and $y = -3$
   b Without drawing the graphs, calculate the coordinates of
      the point where the lines $y = 3x - 2$ and $y = 4 - x$ meet.

4 Find the equation of each line on this graph.

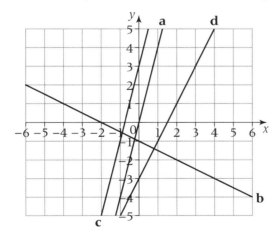

1 Find the nth term of these sequences.

   a 4, 7, 10, 13, 16, ...
   b 2, 7, 12, 17, 22, ...
   c 18, 14, 10, 6, 4, ...
   d 1.5, 2, 2.5, 3, 3.5, ...

2 Find the value of n that generates the term given from each of these sequences.

   a $T_n = 5n - 3; \ T_n = 22$
   b $T_n = \dfrac{n-1}{n+1}; \ T_n = \dfrac{99}{101}$

3 The straight line L_1 has equation $y = 3x - 2$. The straight line L_2 is parallel to L_1. The straight line L_2 passes through $(2, 5)$. Find an equation of the straight line L_2.

4 Find the coordinates of the point where the graphs of $\dfrac{x}{5} + \dfrac{y}{2} = 1$ and $5y = 2x - 6$ meet.

5 Write the equation of the line that passes though.

   a $(0, -2)$ and $(4, 0)$
   b $(-1, 4)$ and $(2, -2)$
   c $(3, 4)$ and $(-1, -2)$

6 Find the equation of line A.

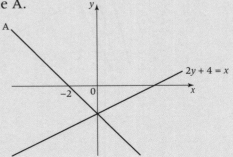

1 Pair these cards together if they show equivalent numbers. Which is the odd card out?

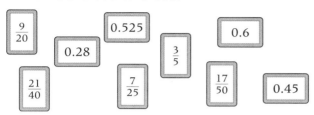

2 Use the formula $r = \sqrt{\frac{A}{\pi}}$ to find the radius of a circle with area 64 cm². Give your answer to 3 significant figures.

3 Write a formula for the area of each shaded region.

a

b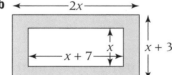

4 a Expand and simplify $(p + q)^2$.
   b Hence, find the value of
   $$2.84^2 + 2 \times 2.84 \times 1.16 + 1.16^2$$

1 By copying and completing this table, state whether a positive number will give a result that is *larger, smaller* or *the same size*.

	The result is larger, smaller or the same size?
× 1.7	*larger*
÷ 0.5	
× 0.9	
÷ 1.25	
× 1	

2 True or False?

   a Dividing by 0.2 is the same as multiplying by 5.
      Show your working.
   b Multiplying by 0.25 is the same as dividing by 4.
      Show your working.

Hint: Use fractions to demonstrate.

3 Work these out using mental methods.

   a 5×0.4 **b** 0.03×0.5
   c $6 \div 0.2$ **d** $0.8 \div 0.04$
   e 0.12×0.6 **f** $1.8 \div 0.03$
   g 1.5×0.15 **h** $2.24 \div 1.6$

4 Work these out using mental methods.

   a 10% of 155   **b** 50% of 284   **c** 20% of 135
   d 30% of 75   **e** 25% of 42   **f** 15% of 120
   g 8% of 25   **h** 17.5% of 16

Hint: Find 10% by dividing the number by 10 and 1% by dividing the number by 100.

5 Work these out using mental methods.

   a $\frac{1}{8}$ of 192   **b** $\frac{3}{8}$ of 256   **c** $\frac{1}{2} \times \frac{1}{4}$ **d** $\frac{4}{7} + 1\frac{1}{3}$ **e** $\frac{4}{9} \div \frac{2}{3}$

Do not use a calculator in this exercise.

1 **a** 297.34 + 109.2   **b** 476.92 − 187.48
   c 65.3 × 9   **d** 27.25 × 0.7
   e 102.4 ÷ 8   **f** 254.7 ÷ 9
   g 13.16 ÷ 0.2   **h** 9.7 × 5.4

2 Calculate these percentages, giving your answers to
   3 significant figures.

   a 52% of £85   **b** 86% of £127
   c 12% of £46   **d** 7.5% of £38
   e 37.5% of £72   **f** 14% of £57

3 Calculate
   a 727 × 36   **b** 292 × 51
   c 329 × 417   **d** 815 × 146

4 Calculate
   a 2464 ÷ 44   **b** 2162 ÷ 23
   c 1767 ÷ 51   **d** 19512 ÷ 36

5 Work out:

   a $\frac{2}{9} + \frac{2}{3}$ **b** $\frac{3}{8} + \frac{2}{7}$

   c $\frac{5}{6} - \frac{5}{8}$ **d** $\frac{1}{2} \times \frac{4}{9}$

   e $\frac{5}{12} \times \frac{3}{10}$ **f** $\frac{5}{8} \div \frac{1}{4}$

   g $\frac{7}{9} \div \frac{2}{3}$ **h** $3\frac{4}{5} - 2\frac{1}{3}$

   i $4\frac{1}{2} \times 2\frac{4}{9}$ **j** $4\frac{1}{6} \div 2\frac{3}{10}$

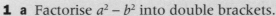

1 a Factorise $a^2 - b^2$ into double brackets.
   b Use your answer to part **a** to work out $7.8^2 - 2.2^2$.

2 a Work these out using mental methods.
   i $\frac{3}{8}$ of 96   **ii** 15% of 240

   iii $\frac{3}{7}$ of 105   **iv** 45% of 160

   b Write these fractions as percentages, using mental methods.
   i $\frac{19}{25}$ **ii** $\frac{17}{20}$ **iii** $\frac{127}{200}$ **iv** $\frac{23}{40}$

   Hint: Find a fraction equivalent to each of these fractions with a denominator of 100.

3 Evaluate
   a $4 \times 3^2 - 7 + 2$ **b** $18 - 7 \times 2^2 + 3^3$
   c $\dfrac{5^2 + 3(10 - 7) + 2 \times 3}{5.72 - 3.22}$ **d** $\dfrac{4.9 \times 3.2}{6}$

4 Evaluate these, giving your answers in standard form:
   a $(1.7 \times 10^5) + (3.2 \times 10^5)$ **b** $(9.4 \times 10^3) + (3.6 \times 10^3)$
   c $(4.2 \times 10^4) + (6.5 \times 10^3)$ **d** $(8.6 \times 10^5) - (3.5 \times 10^4)$

1 The distance from Earth to the Sun is approximately 1.44×10^8 km.

    a Change this number from standard form to an ordinary number.

    b If light travels at a speed of approximately 3×10^5 km/s, work out how long it takes for light to travel from Earth to the Sun.

2 Calculate the missing angles:

    a 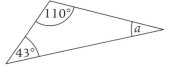   **b**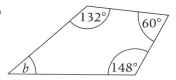

3 Simplify

    a $\dfrac{q^4}{q^8}$ **b** $\dfrac{n^8}{n^3 \times n^3}$

4 Work out these, giving your answer in index form.

    a $x^2 \times x^4 \times x^8$ **b** $\dfrac{a^5 \times a^9}{(a^2)^3}$ **c** $\dfrac{y}{\left(y^{\frac{1}{2}} \times y^{\frac{1}{2}}\right)^3}$

5 If $x = 2$ and $y = -4$, find the value of:

    a $3x + 2y$ **b** $3x - y$ **c** $4y - x^3$ **d** $2y^2 + x^2$

6 Simplify:

    a $2x + 5y - 3x - 4y$ **b** $3ax - 2by + 3bx + 2ax - 6by$

    c $5x \times 3x^2$ **d** $18x^5 \div 2x^3$

1 Solve these equations with algebraic terms on one side.

- **a** $3x + 7 = 25$
- **b** $2(4y - 1) = 18$
- **c** $5(6 - 4x) = 25$
- **d** $3p^2 + 5 = 32$
- **e** $19 = 17 - 2x$
- **f** $22 = 4(5y - 2)$
- **g** $2 + 6x - 3 - 3x = 0$
- **h** $4m^3 - 9 = 23$

2 Solve these equations with algebraic terms on both sides.

- **a** $7x + 5 = 3x - 7$
- **b** $2x - 10 = 7x - 11$
- **c** $9 - p = 4p - 11$
- **d** $3(y - 8) = 4(2y + 9)$
- **e** $2(3 - x) = 5(4x - 1)$
- **f** $14m - (2m + 8) = 1$
- **g** $4(y + 8) - 3(y + 5) = 3(y + 1)$
- **h** $6(x - 2) = 9x - 3(2x - 1)$

3 Solve these equations involving fractions.

- **a** $\dfrac{x + 9}{3} = \dfrac{2(x + 1)}{4}$
- **b** $\dfrac{6p}{5} = \dfrac{8p - 4}{3}$
- **c** $\dfrac{y}{3} + \dfrac{2y}{5} = 11$
- **d** $\dfrac{m}{3} + \dfrac{1}{4} = \dfrac{m}{4}$

4 If I add together one third of my age and one ninth of my age I get 8. If my age is x, form an equation in x and solve to find the value of my age.

5 In 4 years time Clare will be twice the age she was 10 years ago. Use an algebraic approach to determine Clare's age.

1 Change the subject of these equations to that given in brackets.

a $y = 3x + 8$ $\qquad(x)$ $\qquad$ **b** $s = \dfrac{2t}{3} - r$ $\qquad(t)$

c $pq - r = s$ $\qquad(q)$ $\qquad$ **d** $a = \dfrac{b}{c}$ $\qquad(c)$

e $2p - q = t$ $\qquad(q)$ $\qquad$ **f** $\dfrac{a(b - c)}{x} = y$ $\qquad(a)$

g $p(q - r) = a(q + b)$ $\quad(q)$ $\qquad$ **h** $a(x - b) = \dfrac{x}{c}$ $\qquad(x)$

2 Three of these formulae are rearrangements of another three. One is the odd one out. By showing all your working, find the odd one out.

$$a - \frac{b}{x} = c^2$$

$$b = a(x^2 - c)$$

$$\frac{a}{c^2 x} = b$$

$$x = b - ac^2$$

$$ac^2 + x = b$$

$$x^2 = \frac{b}{a} + c$$

$$x = \frac{b}{a - c^2}$$

3 A appears twice in each of these formulae. Collect the terms in A on one side and rearrange to make A the subject of the formula.

a $aA + b = cA + d$ $\qquad$ **b** $Ax + 6 = 2 - Ay$

c $p(A + a) = q(b - A)$ $\qquad$ **d** $\dfrac{3 + A}{3 - A} = x$

e $A + x = \dfrac{2A + 3}{x}$ $\qquad$ **f** $\sqrt{\dfrac{A - p}{A - q}} = \dfrac{1}{2}$

1 Solve these equations:

   a $8x - 9 = 47$
   b $12(y + 2) = 60$
   c $5z^3 - 4 = 131$

2 Solve these equations:

   a $4x + 5 = 6x - 9$
   b $10m - 4 = 14m - 14$
   c $5(3y + 1) = 3(9 - 6y)$
   d $3(z - 4) = 10z - 2(3z + 9)$

3 Solve the equation

$$\frac{3(x - 4)}{x^2 - 16} + \frac{2}{x - 1} = \frac{5}{6}$$

Hint: First factorise $x^2 - 16$ and then cancel.

4 If $\dfrac{3}{x + 2} + 2 = \dfrac{9}{2x + 1}$

Show that $4x^2 + 7x - 11 = 0$.

5 Make x the subject of these formulae.

   a $x + ab = c$ **b** $p^3 x - q = r$ **c** $d + \dfrac{x}{c} = f$

   d $\sqrt{x + k} = 4$ **e** $\sqrt{(n^2 + x^2)} = m$

6 x appears twice in each of these formulae. Collect the terms in x on one side and rearrange to make x the subject of the formula.

   a $px + q = ax + b$ **b** $(x - m) = tx$

   c $\dfrac{x + p}{x - p} = A$ **d** $x(m - n) = p - x$

1 Generate the first five terms of these sequences and comment on the behaviour of each.

  a $T_n = 2^n + 1$ **b** $T_n = \dfrac{1}{n(n+1)}$ **c** $T_n = n^2 + 3n + 2$

  d $T_n = 10 - n$ **e** $T_n = 1 + 3(-1)^{n+1}$

  Hint: Use the words diverge, converge, limit and oscillate.

2 a Without drawing the graphs, write where these pairs of lines intersect.

  i $x = 1$ and $y = 0$
  ii $y = -1$ and $x = -2$
  iii $x = -\frac{2}{3}$ and $y = \frac{3}{2}$

  b Without drawing the graphs, calculate the coordinates of the point where the lines $y = 3x - 6$ and $y = 4 - x$ meet.

3 Choose either 'parallel' or 'perpendicular' to complete these sentences.

  a The line $y = 2x + 1$ is   to the line $y = 2x - 3$.
  b The line $y = 6 - x$ is   to the line $y = 12 - x$.
  c The line $y = 2x - 5$ is   to the line $y = 7 - \frac{1}{2}x$.
  d The line $3y = 4 - x$ is   to the line $y = 3x + 2$.
  e The line $\frac{x}{3} + \frac{y}{4} = 1$ is   to the line $\frac{x}{6} + \frac{y}{8} = 1$.

4 Work these out using a calculator, giving your answer in standard form.

  a $(2.4 \times 10^5) \times (1.92 \times 10^{-3})$

  b $(4.7 \times 10^8) \div (3.2 \times 10^3)$

  c $(1.26 \times 10^{-3}) \div (2.52 \times 10^{-4})$

  d $(6.39 \times 10^4) \div (3.6 \times 10^{-2})$

  e $(2.9 \times 10^6) \times (4.21 \times 10^{-2})$

  f $(1.96 \times 10^{-3}) \times (5.2 \times 10^7)$

1 Work out these, giving your answer as a power of 10.

    a $10^4 \times 10^8$ **b** $10^{12} \div 10^7$

    c $10^3 \div 10^9$ **d** $10^5 \times 10^4 \div 10^2$

    e $10^8 \div 10^4 \times 10^{-3}$ **f** $10^5 \div 10^{-4} \times 10^6$

    g $10^2 \times 10^2 \times 10^2 \times 10^2$ **h** $\dfrac{10^{-8} \times 10^3}{10^7 \times 10^{-9}}$

2 Write each of these numbers as a product of its prime factors.

    a 210   **b** 540
    c 1350   **d** 1750
    e 1694   **f** 4732

3 The area of a rectangular lawn is 90 m². By grouping the prime factors of 90, find all the possible dimensions of the lawn.

    Hint: Remember to include the dimensions where one length is 1 m.

4 Find the HCF and LCM of pair of numbers.

    a 60 and 72   **b** 24 and 40   **c** 24 and 29

5 Find the HCF and LCM of each set of three numbers

    a 24, 36, 60   **b** 48, 72, 240   **c** 21, 63, 504

1 Work out these calculations, giving your answer in index form.

  a $3^4 \times 3^5$ **b** $2^5 \times 2^2$ **c** $a^4 \div a$

  d $5^6 \div 5^6$ **e** $4^2 \times 4^2 \times 4^2$ **f** $x^2 \times x^3 \times x^4$

  g $6^5 \div 6^3 \times 6$ **h** $8^2 \times 8^6 \div 8^3$

2 Simplify these expressions, giving your answer in index form.

  a $\dfrac{3^5 \times 3^2}{3^4}$ **b** $\dfrac{(5^3)^4}{5^2 \times 5^5}$ **c** $\dfrac{(x^8 \div x^3)^2}{x^4 \times x}$ **d** $y^3 \times \dfrac{y^2 \times y^6}{(y^4)^2}$

3 Solve these equations.

  a $2^x = 16$ **b** $y^2 = 5^4$ **c** $64 = (2^a)^2$ **d** $72 = b^3 \times 3^b$

4 Pair these cards together if they show equivalent numbers. Which is the odd card out?

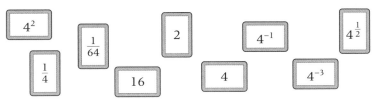

5 Evaluate each of these.

  a $8^{\frac{2}{3}}$ **b** $16^{\frac{3}{2}}$

  c $100^{\frac{5}{2}}$ **d** $81^{-\frac{1}{4}}$

  e $64^{-\frac{1}{2}}$ **f** $25^{-\frac{3}{2}}$

1 Which of these numbers are irrational?

Number	✓ or ✗
$\sqrt{9}$	
5π	
$\frac{4}{7}$	
$\sqrt[3]{5}$	
$\sqrt{15}$	

2 The numbers 1 and 64 both have a rational square root and a rational cube root.

Number, x	Square root of x	Cube root of x
1	1	1
64	8	4

a Can you find the next number that has both a rational square root and a rational cube root? Add it to the table.
b By considering the two right hand columns of the table, work out the next number that follows this criterion.

3 Evaluate these without using a calculator.

a $\sqrt{2} \times \sqrt{8}$ **b** $\sqrt{18} \times \sqrt{2}$ **c** $\sqrt{5} \times \sqrt{20}$ **d** $\sqrt{45} \times \sqrt{5}$

4 Rationalise the denominator of each of these fractions.

a $\dfrac{1}{\sqrt{5}}$ **b** $\dfrac{2}{\sqrt{7}}$

c $\dfrac{3}{1 + \sqrt{10}}$ **d** $\dfrac{1 - \sqrt{3}}{1 + \sqrt{3}}$

5 Simplify these expressions.

a $2\sqrt{5} + \sqrt{45}$ **b** $\sqrt{20}(1 + \sqrt{5})$ **c** $(5 + \sqrt{3})(5 - \sqrt{3})$

1 Work out these calculation and give your answers in index form.

   a $10^3 \times 10^{-2} \times 10^5$ **b** $10^4 \times 10^3 \div 10^5$

   c $10^2 \times 10^{-3} \div 10^7$ **d** $10^{-4} \times 10^{-3} \div 10^5$

2 **a** Express these numbers as products of their prime factors.

    i   750   **ii** 1470

   b By drawing an appropriate Venn diagram, find

    i   the HCF and   **ii** the LCM of 750 and 1470.

   c Find the smallest number that can be multiplied by 750 to give a square number.

3 Evaluate each of these

   a $4^{-\frac{1}{2}}$ **b** 5^0 **c** $16^{\frac{3}{2}}$ **d** $125^{-\frac{2}{3}}$

4 Say whether each of these numbers is rational or irrational.

   a $\sqrt{49}$ **b** 7π **c** $\sqrt[3]{11}$

5 Evaluate these, leaving your answers in surd form.

   a $\sqrt{3}\,(2-\sqrt{3})$ **b** $(8+\sqrt{5})\,(3-\sqrt{5})$

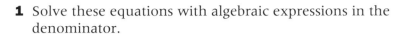

A4 HW1   Check-in review

1 Solve these equations with algebraic expressions in the denominator.

a $\dfrac{5}{x + 3} = \dfrac{9}{4x + 1}$ **b** $\dfrac{3}{4x} = \dfrac{6}{3x - 5}$

2 The sum of the reciprocals of two numbers that differ by 2 is $\dfrac{5}{12}$. Find the two numbers.

Hint: Write the sum of the reciprocals as an algebraic expression.

3 Work out, using mental methods

a $\dfrac{1}{4}$ of 372   **b** $\dfrac{3}{5}$ of 1125   **c** $\dfrac{3}{7}$ of 5915

4 Write these fractions, decimals and percentages in descending order.

a 25%, 0.68, $\dfrac{24}{100}$, $\dfrac{9}{20}$, 0.28, 64% $\dfrac{7}{50}$, 0.56

b $\dfrac{3}{20}$, 6%, $\dfrac{1}{5}$, 29%, 0.07, 50%, 0.3, $\dfrac{3}{25}$

1 Solve these quadratic equations by factorising.

  a $x^2 + x - 12 = 0$ **b** $x^2 + 17x + 30 = 0$
  c $3x^2 - 23x - 8 = 0$ **d** $4x^2 - 1 = 0$

2 Solve these quadratic equations by completing the square.

  a $x^2 + 10x + 21 = 0$ **b** $x^2 + 6x = 0$
  c $x^2 - 8x + 1 = 0$ **d** $x^2 + 5x - 3 = 0$

3 Solve the equation

$$x^3 - 8x^2 + 15x = 0$$

Hint: Take out a common factor and use quadratic methods.

4 Solve:

  a $x^2 + 7x + 10 = 0$ **b** $x^2 + 5x - 14 = 0$
  c $x^2 - 8x + 12 = 0$ **d** $x^2 - 10x - 17 = 0$

5 A function is given by the equation $f(x) = x^2 - 6x + 4$.

  a Complete the square on this function.
  b Hence, show that $f(x) \geq -5$ for all values of x.

Hint: If you square any number, the result is always greater than or equal to zero.

1 Complete the square on these functions and hence write the minimum value of each function.

a $f(x) = x^2 + 4x + 1$ **b** $f(x) = x^2 + 10x + 18$
c $f(x) = x^2 - 4x - 5$ **d** $f(x) = 2x^2 - 4x - 3$

2 For each of these quadratic graphs, find

  i the coordinates of the point where the graph cuts the y-axis

  ii the coordinates of the points where the graph cuts the x-axis

  iii the coordinates of the minimum (or maximum) point of each of the graphs.

a $y = x^2 + 4x - 5$ **b** $y = x^2 - 6x + 9$
c $y = 2x^2 - x - 3$ **d** $y = 3 - 2x - x^2$

3 Sketch each of the graphs in question **2**.

Hint: Be careful with part **d**. Notice that the x^2 term is negative. What does this tell you about the graph?

1 Solve these quadratic equations.

   a $x^2 + 7x = 0$ **b** $x^2 + 9x + 18 = 0$

   c $2a^2 - 8a = 0$ **d** $p^2 + 5p - 36 = 0$

   e $x^2 - 5x - 14 = 0$ **f** $x^2 - 25 = 0$

   g $t^2 - 6t + 9 = 0$ **h** $5x^2 = 125$

   i $2m^2 = 5m + 12$ **j** $y(3y + 10) = 8$

2 Solve these equations.

   a $10x(x + 2) = 3(3x + 2)$ **b** $\dfrac{10}{x^2} + \dfrac{3}{x} = 1$

3 Molly's garden is 4 m longer than it is wide. The area of the garden is 21 m².

   a Show that if x is the length of the garden, $x^2 - 4x - 21 = 0$.

   b Find the two solutions to $x^2 - 4x - 21 = 0$. Explain why only one of them is the length of the garden.

4 These trapezia have the same area.
Find their dimensions.

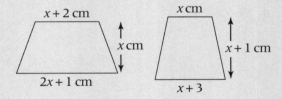

5 Prove that the product of two odd numbers is always odd.
Hint: Let the two numbers be $2n + 1$ and $2m + 1$.

A5 HW1   Check-in review

1 Solve these equations using the method of completing the square, leaving your answers in surd form.

a $x + \dfrac{23}{x} = 10$ **b** $x + 6 + \dfrac{2}{x} = 0$ **c** $\dfrac{2}{x} + \dfrac{1}{x+1} = 1$

Hint: In parts **a** and **b** multiply through by x to obtain a quadratic equation.

2 Work out:

a $3\frac{3}{5} \times 2\frac{2}{9}$

b $4\frac{2}{3} \div 1\frac{2}{5}$

Give your answers as decimals to an appropriate degree of accuracy.

3 Simplify these surds.

a $\dfrac{1}{\sqrt{3}}$ **b** $\dfrac{1}{\sqrt{5}}$ **c** $\dfrac{3}{\sqrt{7}}$

d $\sqrt{20}$ **e** $\sqrt{50}$ **f** $\dfrac{1}{2\sqrt{3}}$

4 Use a written method to calculate.

a 561×49 **b** 298×27

c $496 \div 16$ **d** $966 \div 23$

1 Solve these inequalities.

   a $2x - 5 > 17$ **b** $3(x + 1) \leqslant 2x$

   c $1 + n \geqslant -3$ **d** $3 - 2x \leqslant 9$

   e $\frac{x}{5} \geqslant 7$ **f** $\frac{2x}{3} - 1 < 5$

   g $24 < 8x < 3x + 20$ **h** $x^2 \leqslant 64$

2 Draw a diagram to show the region of points with coordinates that satisfy the four inequalities $y \geqslant 0$, $x \geqslant 0$, $y \leqslant 5 - x$ and $y \geqslant x - 1$.

3 Write down the three inequalities that describe the *unshaded* region.

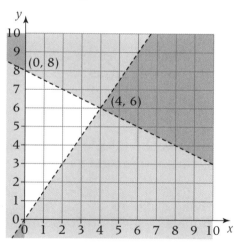

1 Solve these simultaneous equations by the elimination method.

a $2x + 3y = 21$
   $x - y = 8$

b $2p + 5q = 1$
   $3p - 2q = 11$

c $3s - 7t = 27$
   $5s + 3t = 1$

d $y = 4 - x$
   $3x + 44 = 5y$

e $2y = 18 - 4x$
   $0 = 3x - 2y + 4$

f $4a - 2b + 2 = 0$
   $3b - 3a + 3 = 0$

2 Sarah keeps her receipts from a coffee bar. She observes that on one visit she bought 2 lattes and a piece of carrot cake costing £3.25 and on another visit she bought 4 lattes and 4 pieces of carrot cake costing £8.20. The prices have remained stable. What is the cost of a latte and the cost of a piece of carrot cake?

3 In a right-angled triangle, the difference between the other two angles is 12°. Find the two missing angles.

Hint: What is the sum of the two missing angles?

4 A rectangular garden has an area of 40 m² and a perimeter of 26 m. The length of the garden is a cm and its width is b cm.

a Form two equations involving a and b.
b Solve these equations simultaneously in order to find the length and width of the garden.

1 Write an inequality to represent each of these statements, stating the meaning of any letters used.

  a Due to fire safety regulations, the maximum number of people in the theatre at any one time is 354.

  b The temperature of the freezer must remain below $-4\,°C$.

  c Transactions of £5 or less are not permitted.

2 Solve these inequalities.

  a $5x - 9 < 11$ **b** $3x + 1 \geqslant 5x - 3$ **c** $y^2 \leqslant 9$

  d $2(3 - y) \geqslant 3(y + 3)$ **e** $2x^2 - 3 < 29$

3 A rectangular garden has an area of 60 m² and a perimeter of 34 m. The length of the garden is a cm and its width is b cm.

  a Form two equations involving a and b.

  b Solve these equations simultaneously in order to find the length and width of the garden.

4 Solve these pairs of simultaneous equations.

  a $x + y = 5$ **b** $4a + b = 7$ **c** $2p - 3q = 7$

      $3x - y = 11$ $3a + 2b = 4$ $5p - 2q = 1$

5 Draw suitable diagrams to show these inequalities. Remember to leave the required region *unshaded*.

  a $x \leqslant 5$ **b** $y \geqslant -1$ **c** $x < 5$ and $y < 4$

  d $-3 \leqslant x \leqslant 2$ **e** $x > 3$ and $x < -2$

6 Solve the following simultaneous equations.

$$y = x^2 - 9$$
$$x + y = 3$$

1 Expand and simplify

    a $5(3 - 4x)$ **b** $6a(2a + 3b)$

    c $y^2(y + x)$ **d** $(x + 3)(x + 7)$

    e $(2t - 3)(t + 5)$ **f** $(p + 7)^2 + 2(p - 3)$

2 Work out these missing angles.

    a   **b**

 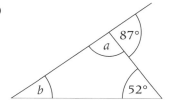

3 Simplify these expressions.

    a $\dfrac{x^5 \times 3x^2}{x^4}$ **b** $(2m^5)^2$

4 Factorise each expression.

    a $4ab - 2a$ **b** $10x^2 - 15x$

    c $a^3b^2c + 3a^2c$ **d** $3p^2 + 9p^3 + pq$

    e $ax + ay - 5x - 5y$ **f** $x^2 + 8x + 15$

    g $x^2 + 5x - 6$ **h** $3x^2 - 10x - 8$

5 Find the surface area of this cylinder.
Give your answer to 3 significant figures.

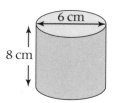

1 Work out the missing angles, giving reasons for your answers.

a

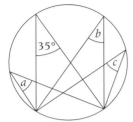

b

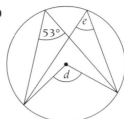

c

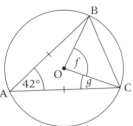

d

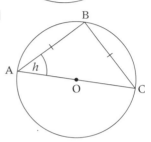

2 Work out the missing angles, giving reasons for your answers.

a

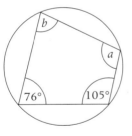

b

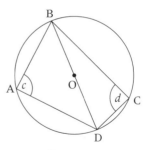

c

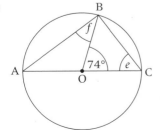

d

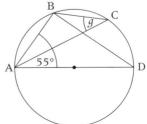

1 Work out the missing angles, giving reasons for your answers.

a

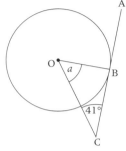

b

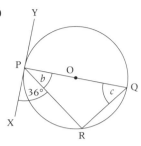

c

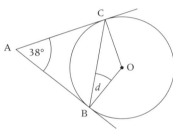

d

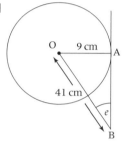

2 Work out the missing angles, giving reasons for your answers.

a

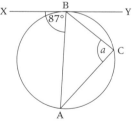

b

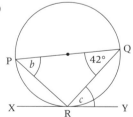

c

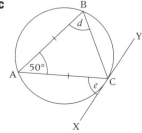

d

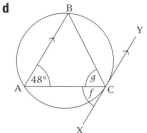

1 Work out the missing angles, giving reasons for your answers.

a

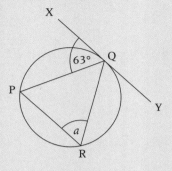

b

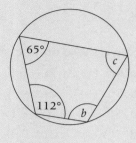

2 A, B and C are points on the circumference of a circle, centre O.

  a Find angle AOC.

  b Give a reason for your answer.

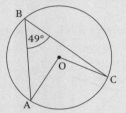

3 **a** Calculate the size of angle PRQ. Give reasons for your answer.

  b Calculate the size of angle QPR. Give reasons for your answer.

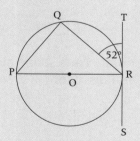

G2 HW1 Check-in review

1 Simplify these fractional multiplications and divisions.

a $\dfrac{x+3}{2} \times \dfrac{6}{x^2 - 2x - 15}$ **b** $\dfrac{x^2 - 4}{24} \div \dfrac{x^2 - 7x - 18}{8}$

2 Solve these double-sided equations.

a $4(x + 3) = 7x - 6$

b $5(a - 4) = 2(a + 2)$

c $5(t + 1) = 3(3t - 1)$

d $5(3 - p) = 3(4 - p)$

e $7y - 2(y - 5) = 20$

f $(m + 4)(m - 1) = (m + 1)^2$

3 Reflect each shape in the dashed mirror line.

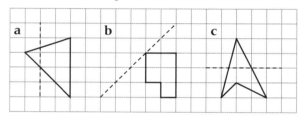

4 Rotate each shape about C, by the given angle and direction.

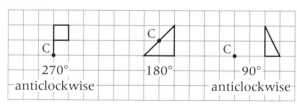

1 Using square grid paper, draw a set of axes.
Label the *x*-axis from −3 to 6.
Label the *y*-axis from −5 to 5.
Draw a shape with vertices (2, 1), (2, 4), (3, 4), (3, 2), (4, 2), (4, 1). Label the shape A.

a Rotate shape A 90° clockwise about (1, 0).
Label the image B.
b Rotate shape B 90° clockwise about (1, 0).
Label the image C.
c Describe a single transformation that maps shape A onto shape C.

2 Using square grid paper, draw a set of axes.
Label the *x*-axis from −5 to 8.
Label the *y*-axis from 0 to 5.
Draw a parallelogram with vertices (1, 1), (2, 2), (5, 2), (4, 1).
Label the parallelogram P.

a Translate the parallelogram P through $\left(\begin{smallmatrix} -5 \\ 1 \end{smallmatrix}\right)$.
Label the image Q.
b Translate the parallelogram P through $\left(\begin{smallmatrix} 2 \\ 2 \end{smallmatrix}\right)$.
Label the image R.

3 Describe fully the transformation that maps

a Triangle A to triangle B
b Triangle C to triangle B
c Triangle B to triangle D
d Triangle D to triangle A
e Triangle E to triangle A

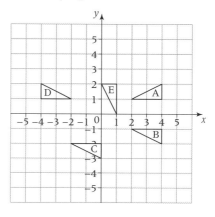

1 Which of these pairs of triangles are congruent? Give reasons for your answers.

a

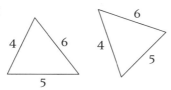

b

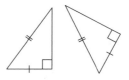

c

d

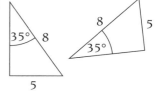

2 ABCD is a square. Prove that triangles ABC and ACD are congruent.

3 Prove that triangle PQR is congruent to triangle RST.

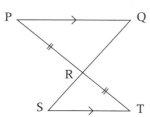

1 Copy this diagram.

a Enlarge parallelogram ABCD by scale factor 2 about centre (0, 0). Label the image A'B'C'D'.

b Enlarge parallelogram ABCD by scale factor $-\frac{1}{2}$ about centre (0, 0). Label the image A"B"C"D".

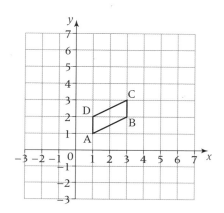

2 Triangle A'B'C' is an enlargement of triangle ABC.

a Copy the diagram and, showing clearly any pencil lines you use to help you, find the centre of enlargement.

b Write the scale factor of this enlargement.

c What is the scale factor of the enlargement that maps triangle A'B'C' back onto triangle ABC? What do you notice about this and your answer to part **b**?

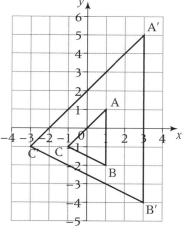

3 Are triangles ABC and PQR similar triangles? Show your working.

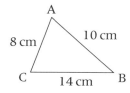

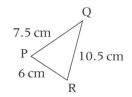

1 a Reflect shape L in the line $x = 0$. Label the image M.

b Reflect shape M in the line $x = 3$. Label the image N.

c Describe fully the single transformation that maps shape L onto shape N.

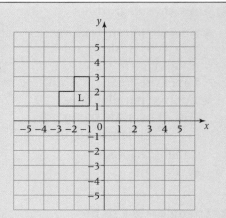

2 This diagram shows a triangle PST.

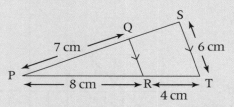

Work out the length of **a** QR **b** PS.

3 PQRS is a parallelogram. Prove that triangles SPQ and QRS are congruent.

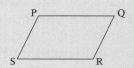

4 Find the missing side.

a

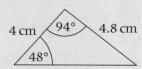

b

1 Sketch these quadratic graphs.

    a $y = x^2 + 2x - 8$ **b** $y = x^2 - 2x - 3$

Hint: Find the coordinates of the points where each graph cuts the x and y axes. Complete the square and find the minimum point of each graph.

2 Find the missing angles.

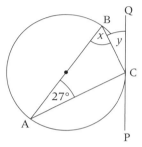

Hint: Look at the line AB. What sort of a line is it? This should help you find the angle ACB in order to proceed.

3 Danesh surveys his form class and finds that 24 out of the 32 children have a pet and 12 of the children do not have their own television. Give your answers as fractions in their lowest terms.

    a What proportion of the children have a pet?
    b What proportion of the children have their own television?
    c What is the ratio of children with pets to children without pets? Give this ratio in its simplest form.

4 Use your calculator to find the value of these, giving your answers to 4 significant figures.

    a $\dfrac{3.241 \times 5.016}{2.897}$ **b** $\dfrac{9.194}{3.127 \times 1.563}$ **c** $\dfrac{1}{0.231} - \dfrac{8.254}{4.176}$

    d $\sqrt{\left(\dfrac{2.564}{1.112}\right)}$ **e** $\dfrac{\sqrt{9.332} + (7.214)^3}{(8.246)^2}$

1 The cost of 8 tins of beans is £2.80. Find the cost of 3 tins of beans. Show all your working.

Hint: Use the unitary method and find the price of one tin.

2 The mass of gold, g, is directly proportional to its volume, v.

  a Given that 200 cm³ of gold has a mass of 3864 g, find a formula connecting g and v.

  b Find the mass of a gold bar, in kilograms, with dimensions 20 cm by 8 cm by 4 cm.

  c Find the volume of a gold bar with a mass of 46.368 kg. Suggest a reasonable set of dimensions for this gold bar.

3 The cost, C, of carpeting a room is directly proportional to the area, a, of that room.

  a Given that the cost of 7.5 m² of carpet for Rebecca's bedroom is £168.75, find a formula connecting C and a.

  b Use your formula to find the cost of carpeting the lounge, which has an area of 14.5 m², in the same carpet.

  c The dining room costs £236.25 to cover in the same carpet. What is the area of the dining room?

4 P varies with the square of q. If $P = 51.2$ when $q = 3.2$

  a find a formula for P in terms of q

  b find the value of P when $q = 0.3$

  c find the value of q when $P = 16.2$.

5 Given that y is directly proportional to the cube root of x and that y is 12 when x is 8, find

  a a formula connecting y and x

  b the value of x when y is 24.

Hint: Writing $\sqrt[3]{x}$ as $x^{\frac{1}{3}}$ is more usual in formulae.

1 A Mathematics department wants to buy new textbooks. The amount, A, that the department can afford per textbook is inversely proportional to the number of textbooks, n, that they decide to buy.

  a Given that the department calculates that it can afford 30 books at £14 each, find a formula connecting A and n.

  b What is the budget for this set of textbooks?

  c Use your formula to find the amount that they can afford to spend on each book if they wish to have 35 textbooks in this set.

  d The Mathematics department decide to buy *Fab Maths* at a cost of £10.50 per book. How many books can they buy?

2 y varies inversely with the square of x.
If $y = 12.8$ when $x = 5$,

  a find a formula for y in terms of x

  b find the value of y when $x = 2$

  c find the value of x when $y = 5$.

3 The variable y is inversely proportional to the variable x. Write the effect on y if x is

  a multiplied by 2   **b** divided by 5

  c multiplied by 0.25   **d** divided by 0.8

4 y is inversely proportional to x. If $y = 20$ when $x = 16$, find

  a a formula for y in terms of x

  b the value of y when $x = 10$

  c the value of x when $y = 15$.

5 The number of people, n, required to build a wall is inversely proportional to the time taken, t.

  a Given that it takes 10 people 4 hours to build this wall, find a formula connecting t and n.

  b How long would it take 8 people to build this wall?

  c How many people are required to build the wall in just 20 minutes?

1 350g of organic tomatoes cost £ 1.61. Calculate the cost of 950g of the same tomatoes.

2 If a varies as b and $a = 6$ when $b = 10$, find

   a the value of a when $b = 18$
   b the value of b when $a = 9$.

3 y is proportional to the square of z.
  When $y = 39.2$, $z = 2.8$

   a Write a formula for y in terms of z.
   b Calculate y when $z = 4.3$
   c Calculate z when $y = 18.05$

4 The time taken, t (hours), on a journey varies inversely as the average speed, s (km per hour), for the journey. When $t = 2.5$, $s = 48$.

   a Write a formula for t in terms of s.
   b Calculate the value of t when $s = 50$.

1 a Copy the graph and enlarge triangle ABC by scale factor 3 about centre (0, 3). Label the image A'B'C'.

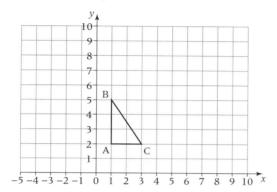

b On the same graph, enlarge triangle ABC by scale factor −1 about centre (0, 3). Label the image A"B"C".

2 ABC is an isosceles triangle where AB = BC. A line has been drawn from B to meet the base, AC, at D. BD is perpendicular to AC. Prove that triangles BAD and BDC are congruent.

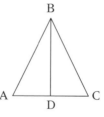

Hint: Use **R**ight-angle, **H**ypotenuse, **S**ide.

3 If I add together one quarter of my age and one sixteenth of my age I get 10. If my age is x, form an equation in x and solve to find the value of my age.

4 Solve these equations involving fractions.

a $\dfrac{x + 4}{2} = \dfrac{3(x + 6)}{5}$ **b** $\dfrac{2x}{5} = \dfrac{4(x - 1)}{9}$

For all questions, give your answers to 1 decimal place.

1 Find the area of each sector.

a
40° 16 mm

b
100° 9 cm

c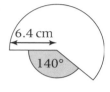
6.4 cm 140°

d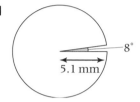
8° 5.1 mm

2 Find the perimeter of each of the sectors in question **1**.

3 Find each of the shaded angles.

a arc length = 4.2 cm
5 cm

b arc length = 24 m
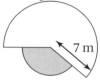
7 m

c Area = 65 m²
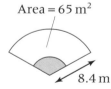
8.4 m

d arc length = 58.9 mm
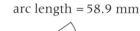
75 mm

4 Find the volume of each solid.

a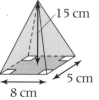
15 cm
5 cm
8 cm

b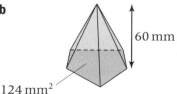
60 mm
124 mm²

c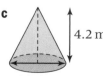
4.2 m
12.6 m

G3 HW3 Surface areas of pyramids and cones

For all questions, give your answers to 3 significant figures.

1 Find the surface area of each solid.

  a Regular tetrahedron of side 4 cm.

  b Square-based pyramid, base length = 10 cm, vertical height above mid-point of square base = 12 cm.

2 Find the curved surface area of each cone.

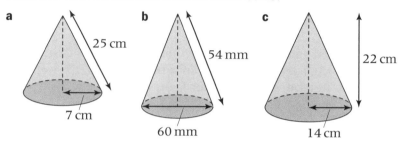

  a 25 cm, 7 cm

  b 54 mm, 60 mm

  c 22 cm, 14 cm

Hint: Use the formula: Curved surface area of cone = πrl

3 Both of these sectors are folded to form cones. Find the curved surface area of each cone.

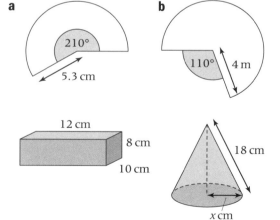

  a 210°, 5.3 cm

  b 110°, 4 m

4 The cuboid and cone have the same surface area. Find the radius of the base of the cone.

12 cm, 8 cm, 10 cm, 18 cm, x cm

1 A metal sphere of radius 8 cm is to be melted down to make 10 smaller spheres of equal volume. Find the radius of a small sphere.

Hint: Find the volume of the large sphere using $v = \frac{4}{3}\pi r^3$ and divide by 10. Use the formula again to find r.

2 A solid metal sphere of radius 3 cm is melted down to form a cone of base radius 3 cm. Work out the height of the cone.

3 The curved surface area of a cylinder, radius r, is the same as the surface area of a sphere, radius $2r$. Show that the height of the cylinder is $8r$.

Hint: Calculate the surface area of the sphere, radius $2r$, leaving the answer in terms of π and r. Do the same for the curved surface area of the cylinder. Find h, the height of the cylinder.

4 A bowling alley wants to buy chutes down which children can bowl in order to direct their aim at the pins. Children's bowling balls have a surface area of 5025 cm². The chute must have 3 cm room around the ball in order to allow it to move freely.
What is the minimum diameter the chute can have?

Hint: Rearrange the formula for the surface area of a sphere and hence find the diameter of the bowling ball.

For all questions, give your answers to 1 decimal place.

1 Find **i** the volume and **ii** the surface area for each sphere.

a 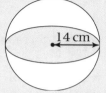 14 cm

b 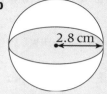 2.8 cm

c 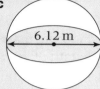 6.12 m

2 A sphere has a surface area of 100 cm². Calculate the volume of the sphere.

Hint: Find the radius of the sphere using the formula:
Surface area = $4\pi r^2$

3 A child's toy consists of a cone attached to a hemisphere. The radius of the hemisphere is 3 cm and the total height of the toy is 7 cm. Find

a the volume of the toy

b the surface area of the toy.

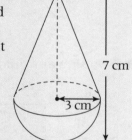
7 cm
3 cm

4 Find the volume of this frustrum, giving your answer to 3 significant figures.

Hint: First, use similar triangles to find the height of the complete cone. Consider the problem as the difference in volume between a large and small cone.

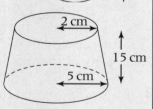
2 cm
15 cm
5 cm

5 The scale factor of a map is 1 : 20 000.

a What length, in metres, does 1 cm on the map represent?

b A plot of land is represented by 2 cm² on the map. How large, in square metres, is the actual plot of land?

1 The mass, M, of copper, is directly proportional to its volume, V.

   a Given that 150 cm³ of copper has a mass of 1344 g, find the value of ρ in the formula $M = \rho V$.

   b What property of copper does the value ρ represent?

   c Find the mass of a solid copper rod of radius 1.5 cm and length 30 cm.

   d Find the volume of a solid copper rod with a mass of 2.912 kg.

2 a Find the area of this sector.   **b** Calculate the missing angle.

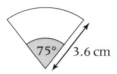
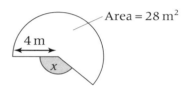

3 Two similar cylinders have diameters of 5 cm and 8 cm.

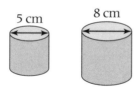

   If the capacity of the larger cylinder is 384 cm³, find the capacity of the smaller cylinder.

4 If y is proportional to the square of x and when $x = 3$, $y = 27$, calculate

   a the value of y when $x = 4$

   b the value of x when $y = 75$.

1 Calculate the length of the missing sides.

a
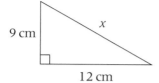

b
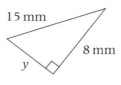

c
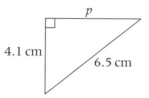

d
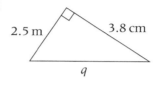

2 A triangle has vertices A = (1, 1), B = (4, 4) and C = (5, 0).

a Sketch a diagram of this triangle.
b Calculate the length of AB.
c The point D is the midpoint of the line AB. Work out the coordinates of point D.
d Calculate the length of CD.
e Using your answers to parts **b** and **d**, calculate the area of the triangle.

3 Using the tangent ratio, calculate the length of the missing sides of these triangles.

a
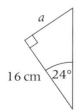

b

c
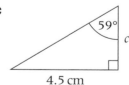

1 Find the missing sides in each of these right-angled triangles, giving your answers to 3 significant figures.

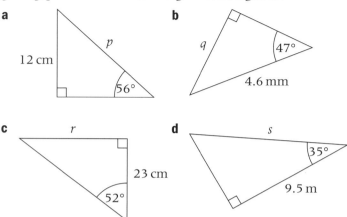

a

12 cm

p

56°

b

q

47°

4.6 mm

c

r

23 cm

52°

d

s

35°

9.5 m

2 Find the missing angles in each of these right-angled triangles, giving your answers to 3 significant figures.

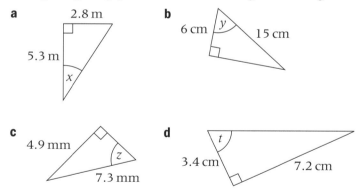

a

2.8 m

5.3 m

x

b

6 cm

y

15 cm

c

4.9 mm

z

7.3 mm

d

t

3.4 cm

7.2 cm

3 Phil measures the angle of elevation from the ground where he is lying to the top of a cliff as 23°. He is exactly 60 m from the base of the cliff. By sketching a diagram and using trigonometry, work out the height of the cliff.

1 Find the missing sides in these diagrams.

a   **b**

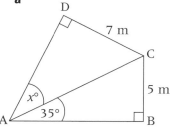

2 Find the missing angles in these diagrams.

a   **b**

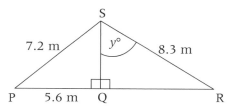

3 A mountain is 1200 m high.
Due South of the mountain is Alphaville, from which the
angle of elevation of the summit is 23°.
Due East of the mountain is Betatown, from which the angle
of elevation of the summit is 35°.
What is the distance between Alphaville and Betatown?

4 The base ABCD of a cuboid is
8 cm by 15 cm.
The diagonal AG makes an
angle 37° with the base of the
cuboid.
What is the volume of the
cuboid?

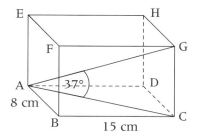

1 A flagpole BD is secured by two ropes from the top of the flagpole to the ground at points A and C. The angle of elevation of B from A is 53°. The angle of elevation of B from C is 34°. The length of rope BA is 10 m. Find the length of rope BC.

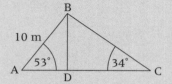

2 In the triangle PQR, RS is perpendicular to PQ. PR = 8.2 cm, QS = 9.5 cm and angle RQS = 38°. Calculate x to 1 decimal place.

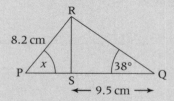

3 ABC is a right-angled triangle.
CD : DB = 1 : 2
Angle ABC = 43° and
AC = 14 m.
Calculate angle CAD.

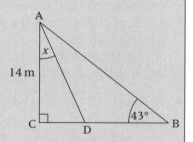

4 An isosceles triangle has sides of length 6 cm, 6 cm and 4 cm.
Calculate the interior angles and the height of the triangle.

1 a varies in direct proportion to the square of b.
Copy and complete this table of values of a and b.

a	2	8	
b	2		5

2 Solve these simultaneous equations.

a $x^2 + y = 88$
    $y = 7$

b $6y - x^2 = 23$
    $y = 8$

c $y = x^2 + 3$
    $y = 3x + 7$

d $p = 3q^2$
    $p = 7q - 2$

3 Calculate these, leaving π in your answers.

a The area of a circle of diameter 14 cm.
b The volume of a hemisphere of radius 6 m.
c The radius of a circle of circumference 18 mm.

4 The sector shown is folded to form a cone.
Find the curved surface area of the cone.

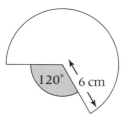

120° 6 cm

5 Evaluate these *without* using a calculator. Show each stage in
your working clearly.

a $\dfrac{-5.3 + (4 \times 3.2)}{5 \times 0.3}$

b $2.5^2 - \dfrac{3.05 + 1.15}{\sqrt{0.64}}$

1 Solve these quadratic equations using the quadratic equation formula, giving your answers to 3 significant figures.

   a $x^2 + 8x + 3 = 0$
   b $3a^2 - 6a - 1 = 0$
   c $2t^2 = 5t - 1$
   d $4t^2 + 2 = 7t$

2 The perpendicular height of a triangle is 3 cm less than the length of its base. The area of the triangle is 27 cm². Form a quadratic equation to represent the information and solve to find the dimensions of the triangle.

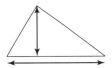

3 The area of a rectangle is 21 cm² and its perimeter is 20 cm. The length of the rectangle is x cm and its width is y cm.

   a Write equations for the area and perimeter in terms of x and y.
   b Use substitution in order to form a quadratic equation in one variable.
   c Solve to find the dimensions of the rectangle.

4 A rectangle has width $= \dfrac{2x^2 + 7x - 15}{4}$ and length $= \dfrac{48}{2x - 3}$.

The area of this rectangle is 96 cm².
By forming an equation in x, find the value of x and hence the dimensions of the rectangle.

1 Solve these quadratic equations using the quadratic equation formula, giving your answers to 3 significant figures.

   a $x^2 + 5x + 1 = 0$ **b** $2a^2 - 4a + 1 = 0$
   c $3x^2 + 7x - 2 = 0$ **d** $3p^2 = 6p + 2$
   e $3x - 7x^2 + 5 = 0$ **f** $5t^2 + 3 = 9t$

2 Solve these equations, giving your answers to 3 significant figures.

   a $x + \dfrac{2}{x} = 7$ **b** $x - \dfrac{3}{x} = 5$ **c** $\dfrac{2}{x + 3} + \dfrac{1}{2x + 1} = 4$

3 Jack is five years older than his wife, Florence.
The product of their ages is 1050.
Let Jack's age be x. Form an equation in x and solve to find how old Jack and Florence are.

4 Solve these by writing them as quadatic eqnations

   a $x^2 + 4 = 5x$ **b** $(x - 3)^2 = 10$

1 **a** Write $f(x) = 2x^2 - 16x + 9$ in the form $f(x) = a(x + b)^2 + c$ where a, b and c are to be determined.
  b Hence, give the minimum value of $f(x)$.
  c For what value of x does this occur?

2 Prove that $y = x^2 - 4x + 4$ is positive for all values of x.

3 Jamie's garden is twice as long as it is wide. The area of the garden is 162 m².
  a Write the area of the garden in square centimetres.
  b Calculate the length and width of the garden.
  c Jamie wants to construct a path to run along the diagonal of the garden. Calculate the length of this path.

4 Work out the angles marked with letters.

a 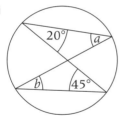 **b**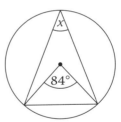

1 Find AB.

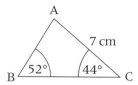

2 In triangle PQR, angle QPR = 54°, angle PQR = 32° and PR = 10 mm. Find the two missing sides of the triangle.

Hint: Find angle QRP.

3 In triangle ABC, angle BAC = 63°, AB = 3.3 cm and BC = 4.1 cm. Find the two missing angles of the triangle.

4 In triangle ABC, angle BAC = 84°, angle ABC = 52° and BC = 12 mm. Find the two missing sides of the triangle.

Hint: Find angle BCA and use the sine rule.

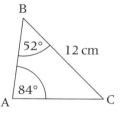

1 Use the cosine rule to find the missing sides, marked with letters.

a

```
        C
      /   \
12 cm/      \ x
    /        \
   /72°       \
  A------------B
     15 cm
```

b
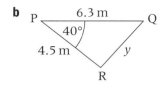

2 Use the cosine rule to find the missing angles, marked θ.

a
```
C\   14 mm
 θ_____
10 mm\      \ B
      \   8 mm
       A
```

b
```
          R
        / |
8.3 cm/   | 6.5 cm
     /  θ |
    P------Q
```

3 Quadville is 45 km from Parallelford on a bearing of 124°. Rhombustown is 60 km due south of Parallelford.
By sketching a diagram and using the cosine rule, find the distance from Rhombustown to Quadville.

4 A triangle ABC has angle ABC = 72°, angle CAB = 64° and BC = 9.3 mm. Find the perimeter of the triangle.

Hint: Find angle ACB and use the sine rule.

5 Find all three angles of triangle ABC.

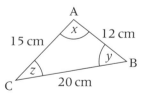

1 Find the area of triangle ABC.

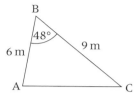

2 The area of triangle PQR is 35 cm².
Find the angle PQR.

Hint: Rearrange the formula $A = \frac{1}{2} ab$ sin C.

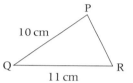

3 Calculate the area of these shaded segments.

a

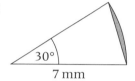

b

4 Marguerite wants to put 1001 sheep in her new field.
Each sheep must have 10 m² of land on which to graze.
By calculating the area of her field, work out whether
Marguerite has enough land on which to graze her sheep.

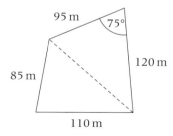

Hint: Draw in the diagonal as shown and use the cosine rule to calculate
its length. Use this length and the cosine rule to find the angle opposite
75° in the quadrilateral. Use Area $= \frac{1}{2} ab$ sin C to find the area of each
triangle.

1 In the cuboid, PQ = 7 m,
QR = 3 m and RS = 4 m.

 a Find PS.

 b Find the angle PS makes with
the base of the cuboid.

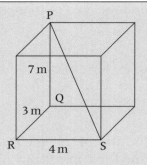

2 a Calculate the area of triangle PQR.

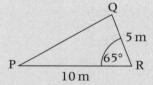

 b T is a point on PQ such that angle PTR = 90°.
Calculate the length of TR.

3 Calculate the area of the shaded segment.

Hint: Find the area of the segment and use Area = $\frac{1}{2}$ ab sin C to find
the area of the triangle.

1 In a chocolate factory, a machine wraps 400 chocolate bars per minute.

   a Copy and complete the table to show the number of chocolate bars, *b*, wrapped for varying lengths of time, *m* (minutes).

m	1	2	3	4	5
b		800			

   b Sketch a graph of the relationship between *b* and *m*.
   c Write an algebraic relationship between *b* and *m*.
   Use this to find
   i the number of chocolate bars wrapped in 90 seconds
   ii the time taken to wrap 10100 chocolate bars. Give your answer in minutes and seconds.

2 Calculate the length of the missing side.

a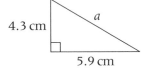

b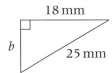

   Give your answers to 3 significant figures.

3 a Rearrange the cosine rule
   $a^2 = b^2 + c^2 - 2bc \cos A$
   to make cos *A* the subject.
   Show all steps in your working.
   b Hence find angle A in this triangle.

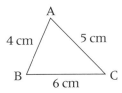

1 a Copy and complete the table of values for the graph
$y = x^2 - 5x + 4$ for $-1 \leqslant x \leqslant 6$.

x	-1	0	1	2	3	4	5	6
x^2				4				
$-5x$				-10				
$+4$	4	4	4	4	4	4	4	4
y				-2				

b Hence, plot the graph of $y = x^2 - 5x + 4$ for $-1 \leqslant x \leqslant 6$.
c Use your curve to estimate the minimum point of
$y = x^2 - 5x + 4$.

2 a Copy and complete the table of values for the graph
$y = x^3 - 5x^2 + 2x + 8$ for $-2 \leqslant x \leqslant 5$.

x	-2	-1	0	1	2	3	4	5
x^3						27		
$-5x^2$						-45		
$+2x$						6		
$+8$	8	8	8	8	8	8	8	8
y						-4		

b Hence, plot the graph of $y = x^3 - 5x^2 + 2x + 8$ for $-2 \leqslant x \leqslant 5$.
c Use your curve to estimate the coordinates of the turning
points of the graph.

Hint: The turning points are where the graph changes from having a
positive gradient to a negative gradient or vice versa.

3 a Copy and complete the table of values for the graph
$f(x) = \frac{6}{x}$ for $-6 \leqslant x \leqslant 6$.

x	-6	-5	-4	-3	-2	-1	0	1	2	3	4	5	6
$f(x)$											1.5		

b Hence plot the graph of $f(x) = \frac{6}{x}$.
c Use your graph to estimate the value of $f(3.5)$.

1 Use the diagram to solve these pairs of simultaneous equations.

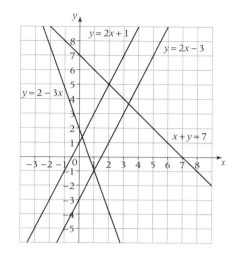

a $x + y = 7$
  $y = 2x + 1$

b $y = 2x - 3$
  $y = 2 - 3x$

c $y = 2x + 1$
  $y = 2 - 3x$

d Using the diagram, explain why $y = 2x + 1$ and $y = 2x - 3$ have no solutions.

2 Solve each pair of simultaneous equations in question **1** algebraically.

3 a Copy and complete this table to draw the graph of $y = 2x - x^2 + 3$.

x	-2	-1	0	1	2	3	4
$2x$	-4						
$-x^2$	-4						
$+3$	$+3$						
y	-5						

b Draw the graph of $y = 2x - x^2 + 3$.

c Use your graph to solve
  i $2x - x^2 + 3 = 0$ and **ii** $2x - x^2 + 3 = 2$.

d By drawing an appropriate graph on the same set of axes, find approximate solutions to $2x - x^2 + 3 = \frac{1}{2}x + \frac{3}{2}$.

e By drawing an appropriate graph on the same set of axes, find approximate solutions to $x - x^2 + 4 = 0$.

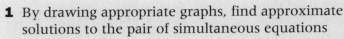

1 By drawing appropriate graphs, find approximate solutions to the pair of simultaneous equations

$$x^2 + y^2 = 9$$
$$y = 2$$

Hint: The equation of a circle of radius r and centre (0,0) is given by $x^2 + y^2 = r^2$[20]

2 a By drawing appropriate graphs, find approximate solutions to the pair of simultaneous equations

$$x^2 + y^2 = 25$$
$$y = 2x + 1$$

b Confirm these solutions by solving the simultaneous equations algebraically.

3 a Plot the graph of $y = 3^{x-1}$ for $-2 \leqslant x \leqslant 4$.

b Use your graph to find an approximate value for x when

    i $y = 2$ **ii** $y = 10$.

4 The graphs of $y = x^2 + x - 2$ and $y = kx$ are shown in the sketch.

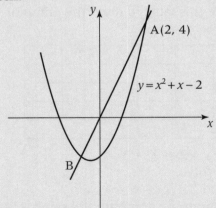

These graphs intersect at A and B.
A is the point (2, 4). Find B.

Hint: Find k by substituting the point (2, 4) into $y = kx$.
Use an algebraic method to find B.

1 Calculate the angles marked with letters.

a
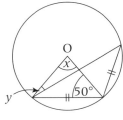

b
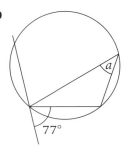

2 Solve these simultaneous equations.

  a $x + y^2 = 22$ **b** $3x - y^2 = 5$ **c** $a^2 + b^2 = 20$

       $x = 6$ $x = 7$ $3a - b = 10$

3 The diagram shows a cone with slant
    height = 4 cm and radius of base = r cm.

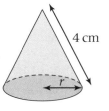

  a The total surface area of the cone is 40 cm².
      Show that $\pi r^2 + 4\pi r - 40 = 0$

  b Hence, find the radius of the base of the
      cone.

4 Find the surface area of these solids.

a

b
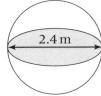

c
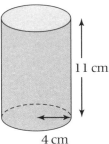

d
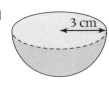

1 Draw these vectors on square grid paper.

$$\mathbf{a} = \begin{pmatrix} -3 \\ 2 \end{pmatrix} \qquad \mathbf{b} = \begin{pmatrix} 6 \\ -4 \end{pmatrix} \qquad \mathbf{c} = \begin{pmatrix} -6 \\ -4 \end{pmatrix} \qquad \mathbf{d} = \begin{pmatrix} 2 \\ 3 \end{pmatrix}$$

a Write a pair of vectors that are parallel.
b Write a pair of vectors that are perpendicular.

2 Use Pythagoras' theorem to find the magnitude of each of the vectors in question **1**.

Hint: Magnitude is simply the length of the vector.

3 OABC is a parallelogram.
$\overrightarrow{OA} = \mathbf{a}$ and $\overrightarrow{OC} = \mathbf{c}$

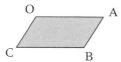

Find, in terms of **a** and **c**
a $\overrightarrow{BC}$ **b** $\overrightarrow{AB}$ **c** $\overrightarrow{AC}$

4 OAB is a triangle.
$\overrightarrow{OA} = \mathbf{a}$ and $\overrightarrow{OB} = \mathbf{b}$

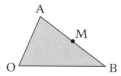

M is the midpoint of AB.
Find, in terms of **a** and **b**
a $\overrightarrow{AB}$ **b** $\overrightarrow{BA}$ **c** $\overrightarrow{AM}$

1 OABC is a trapezium.
OC and AB are parallel.
$AB = \frac{2}{3}OC$
$\overrightarrow{OA} = \mathbf{a}$ and $\overrightarrow{OC} = \mathbf{c}$
Find, in terms of $\mathbf{a}$ and $\mathbf{c}$
a $\overrightarrow{AB}$ **b** $\overrightarrow{OB}$ **c** $\overrightarrow{CB}$

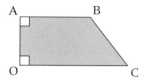

2 OPQR is a trapezium.
PQ and OR are parallel.
$PQ = 3OR$
$\overrightarrow{OP} = \mathbf{p}$ and $\overrightarrow{OR} = \mathbf{r}$
Find, in terms of $\mathbf{p}$ and $\mathbf{r}$
a $\overrightarrow{PQ}$ **b** $\overrightarrow{OQ}$ **c** $\overrightarrow{QR}$

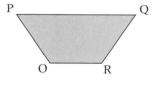

3 OAB is a triangle.
X is the midpoint of OA.
Y is the midpoint of OB.
$\overrightarrow{OA} = \mathbf{a}$ and $\overrightarrow{OB} = \mathbf{b}$
Find, in terms of $\mathbf{a}$ and $\mathbf{b}$
a $\overrightarrow{AB}$ **b** $\overrightarrow{OX}$ **c** $\overrightarrow{XY}$

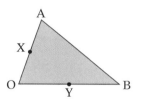

4 OXY is a triangle.
$XM : MY = 1 : 3$
$\overrightarrow{OX} = \mathbf{x}$ and $\overrightarrow{OY} = \mathbf{y}$
Find $\overrightarrow{OM}$ in terms of $\mathbf{x}$ and $\mathbf{y}$.

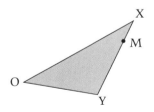

1 $\overrightarrow{OP} = \mathbf{p}$ and $\overrightarrow{OS} = \mathbf{s}$

$\overrightarrow{PQ} = \frac{1}{2}\mathbf{p}$ and $\overrightarrow{OR} = \frac{3}{2}\mathbf{s}$

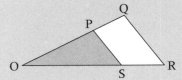

Prove that PS and QR are parallel.

2 ABCDEF is a regular hexagon with centre O.

$\overrightarrow{OA} = 2\mathbf{a}$ and $\overrightarrow{OB} = 2\mathbf{b}$

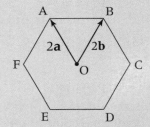

  a Express in terms of $\mathbf{a}$ and $\mathbf{b}$

    i $\overrightarrow{AB}$ **ii** $\overrightarrow{BC}$

  b M is the midpoint of AF.
Express $\overrightarrow{EM}$ in terms
of $\mathbf{a}$ and $\mathbf{b}$.

3 OPQR is a parallelogram.
M is the midpoint of OQ.
$\overrightarrow{OP} = 2\mathbf{p}$ and $\overrightarrow{OR} = 2\mathbf{r}$

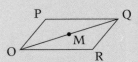

  a Express in terms of $\mathbf{p}$ and $\mathbf{r}$

    i $\overrightarrow{PQ}$ **ii** $\overrightarrow{OM}$

  b Prove that P, M and R lie in a straight line.

  c What can you say about where M cuts PR?
Refer to your working in part **b**.

Hint: For part **b** find $\overrightarrow{PM}$ and $\overrightarrow{MR}$.

1 Solve these quadratic equations using the quadratic equation formula, giving your answers to 3 significant figures.

   a $x^2 + 6x + 3 = 0$
   b $5z^2 - 10z - 3 = 0$
   c $2a^2 = 7a - 2$
   d $3s^2 + 5 = 9s$

2 A wall mirror is shaped as follows:

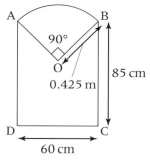

   ABCD is a rectangle where AB = DC = 60 cm and AD = BC = 85 cm.

   AOB is a sector of a circle of radius 0.425m.
   Angle AOB is 90°.
   Calculate the perimeter of the mirror.

3 Prove that triangles OBA and OCA are congruent.

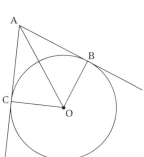

4 Work out the distance between the points
   (5, 4, 6) and (2, −1, 4).

5 **a** Find the height of XY.
   b Find the angle XAY.

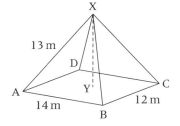

1 Write the equations of the three graphs labelled **i** to **iii**.

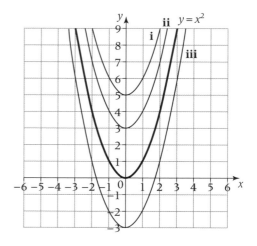

2 Write the equations of the three graphs labelled **i** to **iii**.

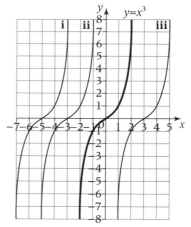

3 The graph of the function $f(x)$ is shown.
What would the points A, B and C be translated to under the transformations

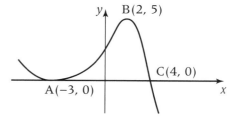

a $f(x) + 2$
b $f(x) - 3$
c $f(x - 2)$
d $f(x + 3)$?

1 Write the equations of the three graphs labelled **i** to **iii**.

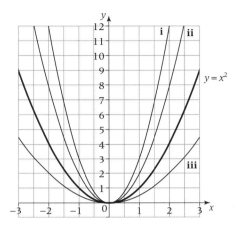

2 Write the equations of the three graphs labelled **i** to **iii**.

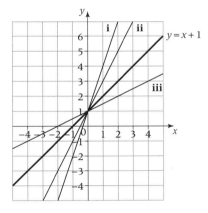

3 The graph of the function f(x) is shown. What would the points A, B and C be translated to under the transformation

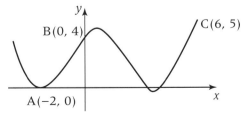

  a 2f(x)

  b $\frac{1}{2}$f(x)

  c f($2x$)

  d f($\frac{1}{2}x$)?

1 The graph of $y = f(x)$ where $f(x) = \sin x$ for $0 \leqslant x \leqslant 360°$ is shown.

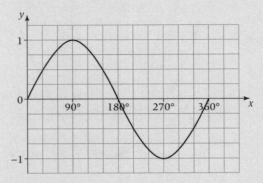

a Sketch the graph of $y = 3f(x)$.
b Sketch the graph of $y = f(2x)$.
c Sketch the graph of $y = 2f(x) + 1$.

2 Describe the transformation

$y = f(-x)$.

3 The graph shows the function $y = f(x)$.
In terms of $f(x)$, write the equations of the functions shown in the following graphs.

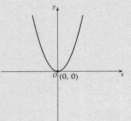

a

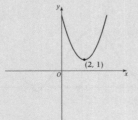

b

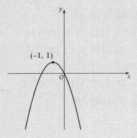

1 The graph shows the function $y = ab^x$.

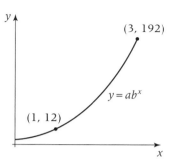

a Given that the graph passes through (1, 12) and (3, 192), find a and b.

b Explain why the curve will pass through the point (4, 768).

2 Use the discriminant to decide

  i the number of solutions that each quadratic equation has

ii whether or not it is possible to factorise.

a $x^2 - 6x - 27 = 0$ **b** $4x^2 - 4x + 1 = 0$

c $5x - 2x^2 + 12 = 0$ **d** $x^2 + 7x - 2 = 0$

e $3x^2 = 2x - 5$ **f** $x(5x - 8) = 3$

3 Solve all quadratic equations in question **2** that can be solved.

4 Make x the subject of these formulae.

a $ax + b = c$ **b** $p^2 - qx = r$ **c** $\frac{s}{x} - t = u$

d $m = \sqrt{n - x}$ **e** $\sqrt{a^2 + x^2} = b^2$

5 The heights of two bottles of water are in the ratio 2 : 5. The smaller bottle has a capacity of 320 ml. What is the capacity of the larger bottle?

6 Calculate the area of the shaded segment.

35°   7 cm

1 We say that each of the sine and cosine graphs has a period of 360° because each graph repeats itself every 360°. Using sketch graphs to help you if necessary

    a for the sine graph, list five values of x for which sin $x = 1$

    b for the cosine graph, list five values of x for which cos $x = -1$.

2 Using graphs, find these ratios. Use a calculator to check the accuracy of your answers.

    a sin 30°   **b** cos 30°   **c** sin 210°

    d cos 330°   **e** sin 45°   **f** cos 270°

3 The first solution to each of these equations is given in brackets. Use a trigonometrical graph to find a second solution between 0° and 360°.

    a sin $x = 0.5$ $(x = 30°)$ **b** sin $x = \dfrac{1}{\sqrt{2}}$ $(x = 45°)$

    c cos $x = 0.5$ $(x = 60°)$ **d** cos $x = \dfrac{\sqrt{3}}{2}$ $(x = 30°)$

4 Using trigonometry, work out

    a sin 45°   **b** cos 45°   **c** tan 45°

    Leave surds in your answers.

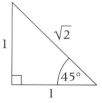

5 Use the sine rule to find a solution for θ.
Use the sine graph to find a second solution. Sketch both solutions.

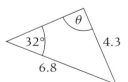

1 A missing angle θ is obtuse. Find θ if

    a $\sin \theta = 0.83$ **b** $\cos \theta = -0.41$

    c $\sin \theta = 0.75$ **d** $\tan \theta = -0.32$

2 Copy and complete this table, using your calculator and question **4** in HW2 to help you.

	0°	30°	45°	60°	90°
sin				$\dfrac{\sqrt{3}}{2}$	
cos		$\dfrac{\sqrt{3}}{2}$			
tan		$\dfrac{1}{\sqrt{3}}$		3	

3 Solve these equations for angles from 0° to 360°.

    a $\sin x = 0.362$ **b** $\cos x = 0.866$ **c** $\sin x = -0.707$

    d $\cos x = -0.289$ **e** $\tan x = 0.412$ **f** $\tan x = 0.577$

4 Draw a graph of $y = \sin x$ for $0° \leqslant x \leqslant 360°$.
On the same set of axes draw and label graphs of

    a $y = 1 + \sin x$ **b** $y = -\sin x$

    c $y = \sin(x + 90°)$ **d** $y = \sin(2x)$

5 On the same set of axes, for $0° \leqslant x \leqslant 360°$, draw graphs of
$y = \cos x$ and $y = \dfrac{1}{2}(1 + \cos 2x)$
Comment on the relationship between the two graphs.

1 The graph of $y = \cos x$ for $0 \leqslant x \leqslant 360°$ is shown.

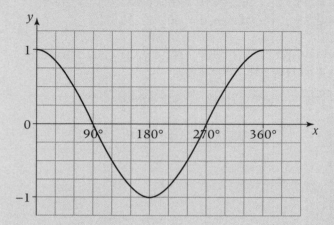

a Sketch the graph of $y = \cos 2x$ for $0 \leqslant x \leqslant 360°$.
b Sketch the graph of $y = \cos(x - 90)$ for $0 \leqslant x \leqslant 360°$.

2 a Use your calculator to find the first solution to the equation

$$\cos x = 0.354$$

b By considering the graph of $y = \cos x$, find a second solution for x such that $0 \leqslant x \leqslant 360°$.

3 Find the solution to the equation

$$\sin x = 0.584$$

if it is known that the angle x is obtuse.